Saving Me First

IV

The Body
and
Zen Practice

By Hui Beop

SAVING ME FIRST

Saving Me First

IV

The Body
and
Zen Practice

Dedication

This book is dedicated to
all who contribute to humanity
and inspire us to learn, to grow,
and to evolve.

And,
to individuals on their journey of self-discovery,
encompassing the wholeness of
mind, body, and spirit.

CONTENTS

Introduction 10

CHAPTER 1
Understanding Our Body System 12

The Body and Zen Practice... 13

Making Room for Light to Enter 17

The Origins of the Body System Theory.......................19

The Body System 20

Behavioral Questionnaire...22
Kidney (Ki) 22
Heart (He)... 24
Liver (Li)... 25
Lung (Lu)... 26
Stomach (St).. 27

Score Summary...29

How to Understand Scores from the Questionnaire................. 30

What Do the Scores Indicate? 32

Domineering Body System...35

Weak Organs 39

The Body Sends Signals..42

Applying the Scores to the Five Meridians.................................45

  1. Kidney & Bladder 46

  2. Heart 47

  3. Liver 49

  4. Lung & Large Intestine. 50

  5. Stomach & Spleen. 51

Building a Strong Body System 52

What to Eat and What Not to Eat.......................................54

Bringing the Body Back into Balance 60

Kidney-Kidney 64

CHAPTER 2
Reclaiming Ownership..104

Charity 105

Karma 107

The Virtue Account 110

Live as Owner...112

Be the Owner.. 114

False vs. Genuine 116

The False Owner 118

CHAPTER 3
Preparation for Serious Practitioners 121

Self-Prayers 122

Preparing for Enlightenment 125

Pay Debts Off 129

Awareness 132

Koan 135

Chanting.. 137

What to Avoid.. 139

How Food's Energy and Traits Can Transfer to Us................... 141

Four Noble Practices 147

The Noble Eightfold Path 149

Thankful Prayers.. 150

Something's Holding Up Our Progress............................... 151

How the Universe Helps Us 154

The Favorable Cycle 158

Timing 160

How Long Will Enlightenment Take? 161

The Special Invitation 162

What's Comes After the Enlightenment Experience?.............. 165

Introduction

If you are reading this book, chances are that you are on a spiritual journey. What you may not know is that every successful spiritual journey involves taking care not just of your spirit and your mind, but of your body, too. In fact, the only way to make solid, steady progress on your quest for enlightenment is to pay equal attention to your body, mind, and spirit. If any one of the three is missing or neglected, your journey may continue, but your destination will not be reached until all three become one and operate as a single unit.

This book is primarily focused on this most easily forgotten aspect of the spiritual search—the body. In the following pages, you will learn how to pay attention to your body, listen to its signals, and give it the proper nourishment it needs to heal so that it can support you on your journey to enlightenment.

At one point or another, most of us fall onto spider webs of suffering. This unfortunate occurrence can be a result either of our own mistakes or of certain unavoidable life situations. Either way, when this happens, it can create shock, confusion, anger, and many doubts—especially if we have no understanding.

Our instinct is to fight it. But the truth is, fighting it will only deepen our wounds and prolong our suffering.

Instead, meditate on it with the Koan, "What is this?"

Through meditation, we gain wisdom that can save us from bad situations by releasing us from shock, confusion, anger, doubts, and suffering. Ultimately, the wisdom we gain from meditation will provide with us Freedom.

Then, we can truly be owners of our bodies, minds, and lives. As owners, we can move forward freely along our journey to enlightenment, unburdened and without hindrance.

Chapter 1

Understanding
Our Body System

The Body and Zen Practice

Very few people have achieved enlightenment by simply entrusting to the foundation of the True Self. People who have reached their destination may have been working on it for a very, very long time. It's also possible they have only been lightly contaminated by earthly defilements. And some of them have practiced with great temperance and a strong will so that they could endure and cut off any possible wants, desires, or habits.

Through our eyes, they got it easy. But of course, nothing is actually achieved easily. These people practiced every day with great dedication to purify their bodies and overcome bad habits.

For most of us, it's not so easy. Our heavy-duty habits chain us to our Karma. To free ourselves, we must first work to unchain our habits.

Some of us have been on this journey for many years, perhaps many lifetimes. Yet we have not given up. We remain dedicated to walking this path to reach our destination. It's great that we are on this journey. Applaud us.

But in order for us to reach our destination, we need to understand and manage our body system. By harmonizing our body system to expedite the journey, we can avoid and prevent current and future problems.

Why is taking care of our body so important?

Right now, we are ruled by our habits, which have contributed to our current unhealthy body system. If we continue with these habits, we know that we will wind up in some form of pain. These pains are created by our ignorance, and the way we neglect to unblock our system.

What does it mean to be blocked? It means some parts of our body are not flowing properly. This can happen because of many different issues, but most damaging are certain continual habits that have disharmonized the body system.

Why do we need to understand the body system? As with all problems, our body's unhealthy condition will continue until we do something about it. Some people come to understanding quickly, while others might take a very long time to "get it." But if we can't come to some kind of understanding about our body and mind, we risk shortening our life span and maximizing our suffering. If we can't understand our body system, we can't bring it back into balance, and we will continue to suffer. If we continue to be ignorant, neglect our health, and give more fuel to the fire of bad habits, our problems will continue to pile up.

For example, someone with a Strong Heart and Stomach body system does not function very well. To awaken their body, they may have a couple cups of coffee first thing in the morning and have even more coffee throughout the day. Without knowing one's body system, this may seem like a logical thing to do, as it seems to help in that moment—but the truth is it's only adding to the body's problems. Again, adding fuel to the fire.

If we are lucky, we may realize our mistake before it's too late and we continue into the next life, and the life after that, on auto pilot. When we go through existence on auto pilot, we have no true awareness of what we're doing—we may not even care to know. And so we go on repeating the same mistakes infinitely. But when we bring the light of awareness to what we're doing with our bodies, we can change these patterns, and move forward on our spiritual journey.

This not to say that coffee is inherently bad for you—some body systems may even benefit from drinking it. But to a body system like Strong Heart-Stomach, it will create many health issues, including dry skin, crankiness, indigestion, headache, ear ringing, and constipation. If someone with this body system switches from coffee to cranberry or aloe vera juice, it will start to solve many of these health issues. (And it will cost less and less drama.)

But until we learn to understand and adjust our body structure, we will not know what changes need to be made, and pain and suffering will continue in our daily living. When we can take good care of our body system, our journey ahead will be a powerful one, resulting in even more freedom and clarity. It may even become a journey that takes us home sooner.

Making Room for Light to Enter

We have a lot of stuff stored in our system. Some good, some great, some useful, some useless, some disorganized, some no longer relevant, and some just because.

The problem is that with all this stuff, there's no room left over in our system for energy to flow freely through it. And if our body system cannot flow and function as one, then we become physically, emotionally, and spiritually blocked. We need to learn how to create room within ourselves so that light can enter. Without this sense of space, there will be no room for new information to flow through us, either.

For example, we read the same book many times over. We think we understand it, but later we find out that we didn't really get it at all. It's especially easy to misunderstand new subjects, and this includes spiritual practices and learning about your body system.

To learn new subject matter freshly, we need to unload some of the things in our system. Then, we will have the space to learn how to operate our body's manual properly, and our body will function better.

You would think the body's manual would be easy to understand—instead, because of poor information given us by other people who also don't understand the body, it seems complicated. It's like we've been brain-washed. But the truth is, it's not as complicated as we thought.

In fact, the body's operation manual is within us. So far, we have been ignoring it and only following external pop-ups—but when we turn our focus inward, we can begin to decode the truth of the system.

When we are ready to begin this inner journey of understanding ourselves, there are many ways that can help us improve our odds of success. Some come naturally, some we must work on to improve.

No matter how we go about it, the fact remains: We need to understand our body system, as well as how to maintain it.

The Origins of the Body System Theory

This particular theory appeared in ancient Gojoseon. Hermits living deep in the forest developed ancient medicine and with awakened eyes saw the movements of the stars and the changing seasons. They realized how it was all connected, and thus established the Chun-Moon (astrological) theory.

What the Chun-Moon theory describes existed from the beginning of time. They simply realized this, and it was put into writing.

They saw beneath the surface and began to read the land, mountains, rivers, and seas, and through established the Ji-ri (feng shui) geomatic theory.

They also read about the human body structures. They saw in it a small universe where all the organs and meridians were interconnected, each playing a role in how it functioned together.

This is what we know as Eastern medicine.

The Body System

Each of us has a unique body system that requires different care. Our goal here is to help you maintain your unique body structure while safely reaching for the True Self.

Over time, a few people discovered a way to solve their problems and reach their desired destination. Having walked this path before, these people knew how to equip themselves so that they could finally arrive. So, for them this is no accidental arrival.

Some of us may want to embark on a similar journey, but without knowledge and understanding, we are likely to face many obstacles. Understanding and preparation are also part of the journey.

Understanding the body system is essential to our survival as we reach for the destination. When some of our body functions are sick, we won't be able to continue until they are fixed. We must therefore take care of these matters before embarking on a spiritual practice.

For example, when we have an imbalanced body system that results from an excess Kidney system, we are overwhelmed by negativity, anger, sadness, invasiveness, etc. No meaningful practice will happen.

This is not to say that someone with a balanced body system will not face obstacles on their journey as well. Every journey will encounter obstructions. But with the body in balance, progress will be significantly easier.

Behavioral Questionnaire

We sometimes confuse our innate organ traits with behavioral and emotional responses that have been conditioned by our upbringing and our environment. When taking the test, please keep in mind that this is to identify traits that are naturally inherent in your personality—not something that was learned, you wish for, or aspire to.

Please answer each question as it best applies to you by circling Y (yes) or N (no). Give 10 points for each Y and tally the score at the bottom of each section. For example: 5 Ys would equal 50 points. If you agree with the statements halfway, then you can give it 5 points.

Kidney (Ki)

I'm a good researcher with the
mental capacity to match. 　　　　　　　　Y　　　N

I am very intelligent, but I often have
gloomy and pessimistic thoughts. 　　　　Y　　　N

I talk a lot or have been told/received hints that I talk excessively.	Y	N
I have a hard time moving on or become afraid to let things go.	Y	N
I have a very curious mind that wants to know how things work.	Y	N
I experience my fears deeply.	Y	N
In my introspection, I tend to relive past events repeatedly.	Y	N
My mind is always thinking up new creations or new ways to do things and understand the flow of money and information.	Y	N
I don't have a lot of faith in mankind or other people, and often feel anxious.	Y	N
I should probably be less moody and sensitive and be more forgiving.	Y	N

Ki totals _____

Heart (He)

Socially, I am an outgoing person.	Y	N
I see myself as an easy-going, cheerful, and sociable person.	Y	N
I tend to talk a lot to gain attention or an audience.	Y	N
I really enjoy shopping.	Y	N
I enjoy people and make friends easily, happily hosting parties and events for friends and family.	Y	N
I don't mind simultaneously belonging to several different organizations.	Y	N
I like attention and being popular.	Y	N
I like to live my life as freely as possible, without rules and obligations.	Y	N
My friends would describe me as an extrovert.	Y	N

He totals _____

Liver (Li)

I seldom get angry.	Y	N
I have a natural tendency to promote, educate, and mentor people in hopes of improving their lives.	Y	N
I am kind, gentle, and believe in mankind.	Y	N
I have a great memory system and am able to retain vast amounts of knowledge.	Y	N
I am proud and would like to be respected.	Y	N
I tend to display indecisiveness.	Y	N
It usually takes something drastic to get me upset.	Y	N
I am kind and gentle to all humans and animals.	Y	N
I often have trouble finishing things that I've started.	Y	N
My friends would describe me as an introvert.	Y	N

Li totals _____

Lung (Lu)

I am very independent, centered, and
fiercely competitive.   Y   N

I have keen and investigative eyes and
correctly assess situations, following
through to the end to achieve what
needs to be done.   Y   N

I have a strong and stocky physical build.   Y   N

A strong will to follow through to the end
is one of my best assets.   Y   N

I get directly to the point rather than beat
around the bush.   Y   N

I am self-motivated and always well- organized
with long-range goals.   Y   N

In the past, I have put myself at risk to do what
was right and just.   Y   N

I can't stand injustice and corruption and will
act to correct it.   Y   N

My communication style is direct, concise, and to the point, and I expect things to get done with no ifs, ands, or buts about it. Y N

I was born to be a strong leader, CEO, or military general. Y N

Lu total _____

Stomach (St)

I am a frugal person. I shop smart, and take good care of my money and savings. Y N

I take comfort in routine and the familiar. Y N

Anything that has to do with money matters to me. Y N

I tend to be indecisive, and I also hold on to old used items just in case. Y N

I don't trust anyone with my money. Y N

I am good at managing relationships with other people and people often view me as a unifier. Y N

I tend to take it personally when
someone opposes me.   Y   N

I tend to hold resentment against people and
fantasize about taking revenge on all those
who have humiliated, hurt, or fought against me.   Y   N

I have a difficult time forgiving and forgetting.   Y   N

I am uncomfortable meeting new people
and exploring new environments or settings.   Y   N

St total _____

Please record all the scores on the following Score Summary Page.

Score Summary

Ki/Kidney   ( )   %

Ke/Heart   ( )   %

Li/Liver   ( )   %

Lu/Lung   ( )   %

St/Stomach   ( )   %

0-30   points Deficient to Weak
35-45   points Good/ Fair
50   points Stable
55-100   points Strong/Above Normal

How to Understand Scores from the Questionnaire

Any organ system that scores above 80-100 is a Double Strong, like Strong K-K, H-H, L-L, Lu-Lu, St-St.
You do not need extra food intake for that food category. Instead, take foods that are meant to support your weaker organs.

Anything above 55-75 score is Strong.
You do not need extra food intake for that food category.

What is considered the Second Strong?
If the next highest score is also above 55, it is described as Second Strong. If other organ systems score lower, but are also above 55, that represents the next Strong, and so on.
You do not need to take extra food intake for that food category.

A score of 45-50 points is stable.

A score between 35-45 is considered okay/fair—neither strong nor deficient. It is functional state unless other events occur.

A score from 0-30 is considered deficient to weak. You will need extra food intake from that food category in order to bring that organ system back to stable ground with a score of around 40-50.

What Do the Scores Indicate?

The score summary from the questionnaire tells us how our organ systems are at work. Depending on whether our body system is strong, stable, good/fair, or deficient, it will affect our journey.

We can continue on as we are with the system we have; we can make some small changes; or we can make great changes. Whatever we choose to do, it's our choice.

But for Zen practitioners, how likely is it for us to reach the destination if we don't make any changes? A true spiritual journey requires us to make corrections as we go along. That's part of our path.

Without change, there will be no progress. Look around. Of all the people who entered this practice, how many reached the top? The ones who never made it didn't make the necessary changes that would have allowed them to arrive at the destination.

Those who do reach the top or destination found a way to fill the gaps and connect missing links during their practice.

When we are out of balance, the imbalance controls our lives: we can't listen, and we won't realize how to fill in gaps or connect missing links. When our body is so imbalanced, we think we can control it with just our will, but this only works for a short time. We give ourselves pep talks, but this also only lasts a short time.

In an imbalanced body system, the strong organs insist that it's their way or no way. The body won't want to eat what's required to support weak and deficient organs and bring the system back into harmony. Why is that? Because our body has been imbalanced for so long, and the domineering organs are in control and don't want to eat any other food items except theirs. The dominant organs don't care if the other organs function better, even though this would actually be in their best interest—if the weak organs are given better support, the dominant organs benefit, too. Instead, the dominant organs want to keep the status quo so that they will not lose control.

But we should care. It's our body, so we must make the necessary choice to feed our weak and deficient organs. At first, our body system might not be happy about our decision and might fight with it. But eventually, the domineering organs calm down after consuming the correct, balancing foods because this actually helps them too. They just didn't know it until we changed our habits. Habits are what got our body system in trouble to begin with. We started one bad habit after another, and these habits became us.

In a highly dysfunctional body system, it can feel like the habits are in control. The habits complain and make rude and unreasonable demands. They've got us in their fingertips and refuse to make any changes. It's like we have given up our duties as owners of our own bodies and left the habits in charge.

But who's really in charge?

We must reclaim ownership of our own bodies and make sure our body system is functioning for us, not for our habits.

Be the responsible owner.

Practice as the owner.

Domineering Body System

Let's say one or two organs have a high score of 70-100. And let's say it's the Strong Lung-Lung or Lung-Stomach and then the remaining scores are below 40.

Pic 1-1

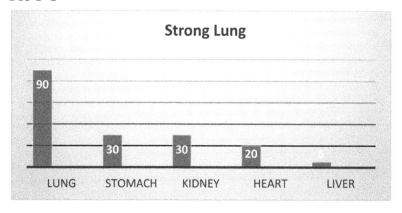

Pic 1-2

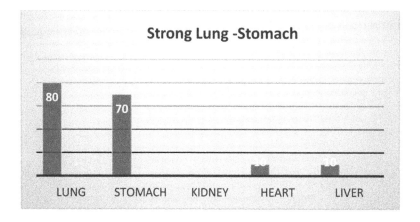

A domineering score reveals that one organ is controlling the rest of the organ system. In this instance, unless we are present as owner to offer different directions, the body system will be ruled by the strong Lung system.

We can liken a domineering organ to a dictator—if it's not principled, it can't be fair to the rest of the body system. But can a dictator be fair and principled? It's a rare case.

Often, the domineering force of the strong organ system relentlessly sends messages, creating craving that we mistake for what the body really needs. Yes, there's genuine hunger or craving for the body, but it's not an easy task to know the difference between what the body really needs and what the dictator is telling us it needs. If we are not careful, we feed the domineering force's needs, resulting in more imbalanced and weaker organs, which will inevitably lead to health problems.

Under this situation, the weak organs can't express their need because they are stopped by the domineering organ within the body system. The domineering organ may send a message to the weak ones to follow its orders: "I will be the one who will make all decisions for everyone. Follow my orders, or else." No respect. And because the other organs are in a weakened state and are unable to offer their support, the domineering organ may feel like it's doing all the tasks.

Anyway, the dictator in the body system claims that there are no problems. That bully system has been going on so long that we have been conditioned to believe in it. But it's not a democratic system—it's a dictatorship within our body system—and it begins to adversely affect our daily lives. If we don't step in and regain control of our own bodies, some of our weak organs may even die. When that happens, part of us has died.

It's the owner's responsibility to be the one in charge of the body system. If we're not, then it's like we're supporting the dictatorship. If the body owner knows the ins and outs of the system, we can take care of it now. But we don't know enough about the ins and outs of our body system yet. Once we understand the system, we can adjust, reclaim our bodies, and make the system a truly balanced democracy.

Once you regain control of your own body system, you can adjust it to function better. Without these adjustments, how are we to fully practice sharing, understanding, loving, and being fair and compassionate? Without making some adjustments to the body structure, our spiritual journey will be fruitless.

Who are we to trust to lead us on a deeper spiritual journey? Remember: our habits and organ functions are not the real owners. If we follow the direction of our weak organs, we won't make it. If we follow the direction of our dictator strong organs, we'll end up broken before we reach our destination. The only safe path is to trust our foundation—ourselves—to be the true owner and lead us forward. With the owner in charge, we can bring balance to our body system and make it functional and healthy. Then, there will be clarity, and we will know where we are going.

Weak Organs

It's crucial to offer support to weaker organs so that they arrive at a fair to stable condition. Until the weak organ is somewhat functional, it can't contribute to the whole-body system, and can't decode the incoming information as it should.

Weak Liver

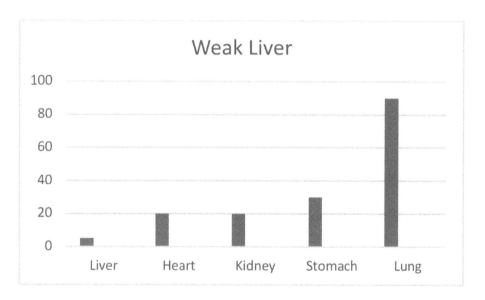

This graph shows a Weak Liver system. Until it reaches fair to stable condition, the Liver system is unable to provide its service to the body. A person with this body system has difficulty understanding kindness and compassion. However, when they give support to the Weak Liver system, they will begin to feel this kindness and compassion throughout their whole body system.

Weak Kidney

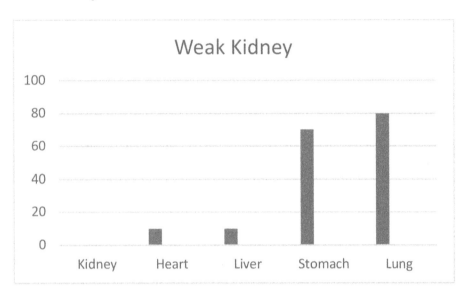

This graph shows a Kidney system with a score of zero. If a person with a Strong Kidney system tries to communicate with a Weak Kidney person, the content of the message won't be understood properly. To decode correctly, the Weak Kidney system must become balanced and stable. Without fixing this situation, we cannot move forward on our journey the way we should.

Above, we have discussed two of the weak organ systems. No matter which of your organs resulted in a low score, the advice remains the same: If you have a weak organ, focus on intaking food that's meant for that organ. This way, it will be a much shorter and more direct journey to your destination.

The Body
Sends Signals

If we pay attention, we will realize that we are constantly receiving signals from our body system throughout our lives. Each incident that occurs, our body tells us what's going on precisely as it happens.

Listen. Get to know the body system and its communication. It will save you from experiencing so much agony, pain, and suffering.

Craving Our Old Program

When we try to bring some balance to the body system, the system resists this and wants to slide back to where it was. Why? Because that's how it was programmed by us through habit. We need to start new habits to bring balance.

Let's say we are trying to bring balance to the Strong Heart body system. By consuming new food, we've brought balance to the system, but that's not the way it feels to the system. The old programming in our body sends us signals or gives us a picture of food we used to eat, urging us to go back to our old ways.

This is different than the body actually craving something—these are just recorded messages that have no truth to them. We must be aware of this and refuse to stay on the old program's auto pilot. As owners, we can tell the body to relax, and let it know that we are not going back to the old program. We are starting a new food regime from now on to bring balance to the body system.

For example, those with a Strong Stomach-Heart may receive the following signals from their body: dry mouth, tiredness, lower abdominal tightness/pain, frequent peeing, burning sensation when peeing, ear tightness or pain, sore throat, aspiration, indigestion, sour mouth taste, constipations, and a lack of energy to do anything else but sit or lay down. These symptoms are a result of a lack of kidney and lung energy.

To solve some of these problems, supply Kidney-Lung energy. The symptoms will disappear once the body stabilizes. If they persist, it means your body is still imbalanced.

If we pay attention to our body system, we will understand our body signals so we can take care of any problems. If we choose to not to take care of it, our body system goes into the next stage of signals, and the next stage of pain and suffering. This may even end up resulting in cancer. Often at this stage, we do not understand how we got here, but it's because we ignored all the body signals in the past.

At this stage, some may choose to try to figure out what happened and what we can do to fix it, but most of us are clueless. They believe our life ends here with this body, and so there's no reason to investigate the roots of their illness further.

But what if this is not the end for us?

What if this ending is only for this body? What if our spirit carries on to another life's journey? If so, we will surely go through the same issues until we fix them. Without adjusting, we will repeat the same things over and over. Without a balanced body system, we can't be a whole person, and we will not be able to reach enlightenment.

Be present with each body signal so you can acknowledge and take care of it as needs arise.

Applying the Scores
to the Five Meridians

Our body belongs to us. It goes nowhere and stays with us no matter what we would like to think and believe. In order to fix some of our problems, we need to understand this first. Then we can examine, verify, and learn from the body's signals, and take care of it.

Use the scores and press spots that are indicated below to confirm if the signals match the symptoms.

When the organ has issues—whether that means lack or excess—it will feel painful. If there's no pain, there's no problem.

Once you've confirmed any potential issue, take care to eat food that delivers support to that organ system, and be aware what's happening with it. If you still experience related pain, it has not reached the required amount. When it reaches the required amount, there will be balance, and the pain will no longer be there.

We all have the potential to become experts in our own body system. When we can take care of our body system right, it's a powerful journey ahead.

To verify the questionnaire's findings regarding body structures, complete the following exercises.

1. Kidney & Bladder

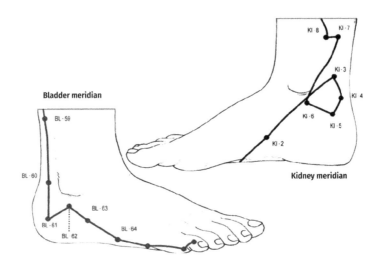

a) Place your second finger slowly but press down strongly the meridian lines and dot points with your thumb to check.
b) If the body system has issues—from weakness to excessive strength—you will feel pain ranging from mild to sharp. It means it needs attention quickly.
c) Rub it to release the pain.
d) See Kidney food & beverages.
e) Rub the Dragon Well to activate Kidney energy.

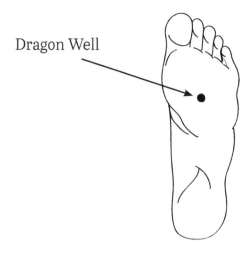

Dragon Well

2. Heart & Small Intestine

If the body system has issues—from weakness to excessive strength—you will feel pain ranging from mild to sharp. It means it needs attention quickly.

Place the fingers of your right hand over your left fingers and press down with your right thumb on the spot to check and confirm.

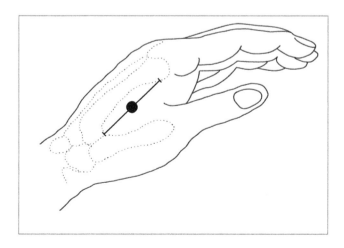

When you make a fist, it will be easy to see this indentation between the palm and the wrist. Press down to check on the health of your heart.

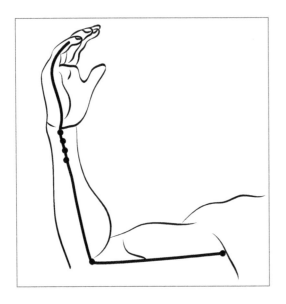

Small intestine, press down on the dotted areas to check for any pain or discomfort.

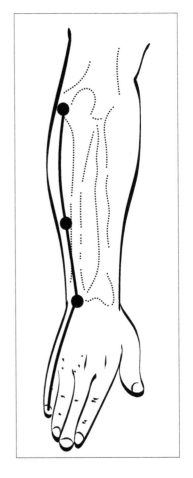

3. Liver & Gall Bladder

If the body system has issues—from weakness to excessive strength—you will feel pain ranging from mild to sharp. It means it needs attention quickly.

Press these meridian lines and points to check and to confirm. Check both feet between bone and muscle.

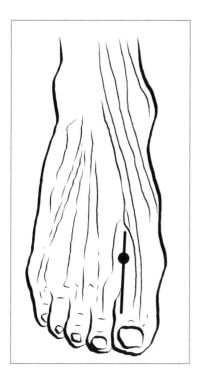 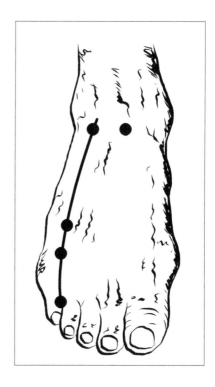

4. Lung & Large Intestine

If the body system has issues—from weakness to excessive strength—you will feel pain ranging from mild to sharp. It means it needs attention quickly.

Press down with your thumb on the dot to check the health of your large intestine.

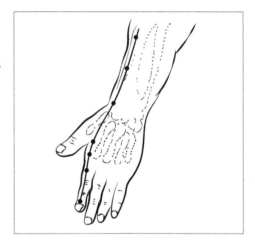

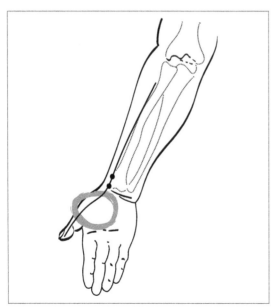

Use your thumb to press down hard on the circle area and the black dots to check for any pain and discomfort for both hands.

5. Stomach & Spleen

If the body system has issues—from weakness to excessive strength—you will feel pain ranging from mild to sharp. It means it needs attention quickly.

Along the meridian line, press down between bone and muscles on both legs to test for any pain and discomfort.

If there's pain, rub the area to release it.

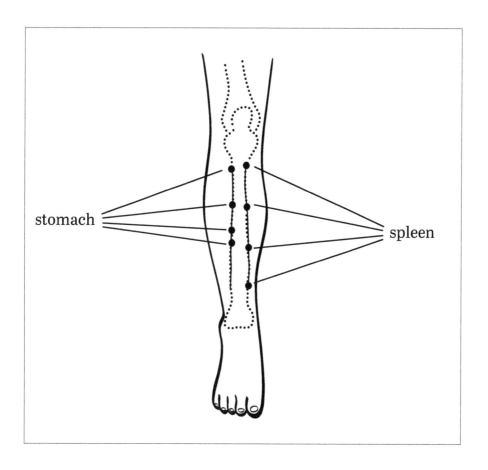

Building a Strong Body System

The easiest way to improve the body system is through changing what we eat. This is something we can do—and sometimes *must* do—for our body to function better. Be sure to supply food or supplements that your body actually lacks—be aware that this is often different than someone's *ideas* of good food. See later chapters for specific food recommendations to help the various body systems.

If our body system is weak in a certain area, be sure to supply plenty of food meant to strengthen that area until we no longer feel a deficit there. Until it is fully charged, our weak organ may be trying to send us important information, but we won't be able to decode it.

Caution

Be sure to avoid all food items meant to strengthen any organs that showed up as Strong in your scores. If you somehow consume the Strong organ food, be sure to add 2-3 times the amount of much needed food items to counter that. Otherwise, the body system will go back to where it was. As we experience these issues, we will find out that it is not beneficial to consume Strong organ food.

As discussed in the Domineering chapter, you may continue to crave the foods that have been established by habit over a long period of time, but if we give in to our old habits' cravings, no improvement can be made.

Harmonizing the body system and bringing it into balance might not fix all our problems. But it will definitely help us to see, understand, and decode what's happening with our bodies, so that we can empower ourselves and make true progress towards where we are going.

What to Eat
and What Not to Eat

The following pages list foods that individually benefit each of the five organs. We choose food items that will nourish our Weak organs and avoid food meant to nourish our Strong organs.

All food items under each section of Kidney, Heart, Liver, Lung, and Stomach will go directly and indirectly to each organ to strengthen or weaken that organ system.

Avoid Strong organ food. The more we eat Strong organ food, the more we'll become imbalanced. For instance, if we are Strong in Kidney system, do not choose food items from Kidney food list.

If we are Weak in the Kidney system, choose food items from Kidney. Many choose not to take Kidney food for whatever reason. However, a lack of adequate Kidney energy in the body system can create many health issues.

In the following tables, the first three items listed are of greatest benefit to that individual organ. There is no limit on neutral food items.

Kidney Food for Weak Kidneys

Consuming these food items will strengthen the Kidney.
The strongest energy items are listed at the beginning.
*An asterisk indicates indirect benefit. Those with diatheses such as food
sensitivity/allergies should check ingredients before taking them.

Grains	Barley, buckwheat, farro wheat (spelt), black rice, purple rice
Beans	Black beans (the tiny ones)
Nuts	Avoid this food
Seeds	Black sesame
Veggies	Bamboo shoots, cucumber, mung bean sprouts, beets, cilantro, celery, zucchini, mushrooms, asparagus, lettuce, chicory, radishes, bitter melon, jicama, watercress, iceberg lettuce, rhubarb
Neutral Veggies	Broccoli, cauliflower, kale, lettuce, onion, parsley, bell peppers
Fruits	Cranberry, lychee, watermelon, durian kiwi, Korean pear, Asian pear, pomegranates, strawberry, blackberry, coconut, *honeydew melon
Meats	Pork, bone marrow, bone broth (stock)
Seafoods	Sea cucumber, sea squirt, edible seaweed (kelp, bladderwrack, sea grapes, chlorella, etc.), octopus, mussels, shrimp
Seasoning	Bamboo salt. Neutral: miso, soy sauce, salt
Oil	Coconut oil, black sesame seed oil
Spreads	N/A
Beverages	Aloe vera juice, cranberry juice, *bitter melon, black oolong, earl grey, English breakfast, barley
Alcohols	Beer
Sweeteners	Avoid if possible
Misc. Items	Mung bean clear noodle, buckwheat noodle, cheese, licorice, cordyceps mushroom, *Echinacea/golden seal

Heart Food for Weak Heart

*Consuming these food items will strengthen the Heart. The strongest energy items are listed at the beginning. *An asterisk indicates indirect benefit. Those with diatheses such as food sensitivity/allergies should check ingredients before taking them.*

Grains	corn, Indian millet, teff, red sorghum, foxtail millet, *wild rice, *corn
Beans	*Pinto
Nuts	Avoid if possible
Seeds	Sunflower, sesame, pumpkin seeds
Veggies	Anything that taste bitter, dandelion, codonopsis, dried mushroom, dried paracrine, radicchio/Italian lettuce, eggplant, lotus root, carrot, tomato, brussels sprouts, cabbage, mugwort, endive, bell flower root
Neutral Veggies	Broccoli, cauliflower, kale, lettuce, onion, parsley, bell peppers
Fruits	Mangosteen, apricot, grapefruit, banana, plantains, passion fruits
Meats	Lamb, duck, quail, chicken, turkey, veal, venison
Seafoods	Squid, yellow dried pollack
Seasoning	Cooking wine, Korean black bean paste
Oil	Extra virgin olive, sunflower, canola, corn nut oils, peanut, sesame, soybean, vegetable
Spreads	Chocolate spreads
Beverages	Coffee, corn tea, ginseng, cocoa, green tea, mocha, dandelion tea, bell flower root tea, chaga tea
Alcohols	Sake, rum, gin, vodka, soju, brandy, sherry
Sweeteners	Avoid if possible
Misc. Items	Ginseng, dark chocolate, rishi mushroom, chaga mushroom, shitake mushroom, yogurt, bee pollen, *Echinacea/golden seal, *Omega 3-6-9

Liver Food for Weak Liver

*Consuming these food items will strengthen the Liver. The strongest energy items are listed at the beginning. *An asterisk indicates indirect benefit. Those with diatheses such as food sensitivity/allergies should check ingredients before taking them.*

Grains	Alfalfa, quinoa, wheat, oat, rye, bulgur, lentils
Beans	All beans except the adzuki and tiny black beans
Nuts	Most nuts except for almonds and pine nuts
Seeds	Perilla, sesame, pumpkin, sunflower
Veggies	Artichoke, okra, bean sprout, arrowroot, avocado, olive, kale
Neutral Veggies	Broccoli, cauliflower, kale, lettuce, onion, parsley, bell peppers
Fruits	Green apple, apples, blueberry, huckleberry, lemon, lime, kiwi, tangerine, elderberry, grapes, oranges, pomegranate, plums, prunes, more berries, raisins
Meats	Chicken, eggs, quail, turkey
Seafoods	All clams (and clam juice) except for abalone & scallops
Seasoning	Miso, vinegar
Oil	Canola, corn, nut oils, extra virgin olive, peanut, sesame, soybeans, sunflower, perilla, grape seed
Spreads	Apple butter, sesame butter, plum, peanut butter, mayonnaise, ketchup
Beverages	Apple, orange, grape plum, prune, omija tea, soy milk, oat milk
Alcohols	Wine, fruit coolers
Sweeteners	Brown sugar, carob, chocolate, corn syrup, honey, maple syrup, molasses, rice syrup/rice malt, sucanat sugar, white sugar
Misc. items	Corbicula extract or soup, flax seed oil, Omega 3-6-9, sour tastes/vitamin C, tofu, soy products, protein power, *echinacea/golden seal

Lung Food for Weak Lung

*Consuming these food items will strengthen the Lung. The strongest energy items are listed at the beginning. *An asterisk indicates indirect benefit. Those with diatheses such as food sensitivity/allergies should check ingredients before taking them.*

Grains	Brown rice, pearl barley, chia
Beans	N/A
Nuts	Pine nuts, almonds, gingko nuts
Seeds	Mustard, mustard green seeds, radish seeds
Veggies	Perilla leaf, basil, bay leaves, rosemary, napa, *cabbage, parsnips, rutabaga, bok choy, chard. (The following items are good for the lungs, but bad for Zen practitioners, as they stir up unwanted sexual energy: all turnip family, mustard greens, mustard, garlic, chives, green onions, onion, ginger, turmeric, radish, sage, arugula, coriander, marjoram, cumin, thyme, cabbage, scallion, fennel)
Neutral Veggies	Broccoli, cauliflower, kale, lettuce, onion, parsley, bell peppers
Fruits	Korean pear, currants, peach, pineapple, banana, nectarine, pear cactus, dragon fruit, jack fruit
Meats	Fish, beef (consume only for medicinal purposes)
Seafoods	All seafood (except squid and octopus)—consume only for medicinal purposes and for a short time
Seasoning	Chili pepper, black pepper, white pepper, dill (beware, as these all also stir up sexual energy)
Oil	Safflower, canola, corn, nut oils, olive, sesame, soybean, sunflower, vegetable
Spreads	Almond butter, butter
Beverages	Mint tea, milk, almond milk, chamomile, pearl barley tea
Alcohols	N/A
Sweeteners	Okay with brown sugar, carob, chocolate, corn syrup, honey, molasses, rice syrup/rice malt, sucanat sugar
Misc. Items	Ginko, Aloe Vera Juice, High quality fish oil, all dairy products.

Stomach Food for Weak Stomach

*Consuming these food items will strengthen the Stomach. The strongest energy items are listed at the beginning. *An asterisk indicates indirect benefit. Those with diatheses such as food sensitivity/allergies should check ingredients before taking them.*

Grains	Sweet rice, corn, white rice, wild rice, proso millet, *sorghum
Beans	Lima, *navy, *pinto, *soy, *kidney
Nuts	Cashews, peanuts, *pine nuts
Seeds	Sesame, pumpkin, sunflower
Veggies	Spinach, cabbage, lotus root, carrot, potatoes, sweet potatoes, yams, winter squash, parsnip, jicama, butternut squash.
Neutral Veggies	Broccoli, cauliflower, kale, lettuce, onion, parsley, bell peppers
Fruits	Dates, figs, mangos, papaya, American pears, cantaloupe, banana
Meats	N/A
Seafoods	All seafood
Seasoning	Cinnamon, ginger, honey, brown sugar, *miso
Oil	Canola, corn, nut oils, extra virgin olive, sesame, soybeans, sunflower, perilla, safflower, grape seed
Spreads	N/A
Beverages	Pu'er tea, corn tea, ginger tea, ginseng, Chinese yam tea, jujube tea, mango juice, goji tea
Alcohols	N/A
Sweetener	Carob, corn syrup, honey, maple syrup, molasses, rice syrup/rice malt, sucanat sugar, white sugar
Misc. items	Propolis, royal jelly, honey, tapioca, bee pollen, *omega 3-6-9, *echinacea/golden seal,

*See pages 45-74 of Saving Me First III: Unlocking for full details of organs and their symptoms.

Bringing the Body Back into Balance

The following 25 body systems show what percentages of certain foods need to be consumed to balance that particular body type.

For instance, if the diagram shows Stomach 50% Heart 50%, select half of your items from Stomach food and half from Heart food.

Food to Stabilize **Strong Kidney**

Recommended food intake percentages:

1) For the first 3 months, 50% Stomach food, 50% Heart food.

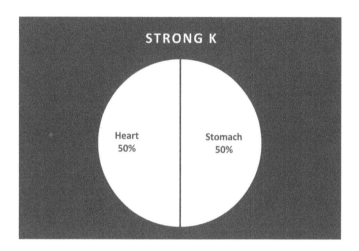

2) Then 40% Stomach food, 40% Heart food, 10% Lung food, 10% Liver food. Consume Stomach and Heart food first, then move on to foods for the other organs.

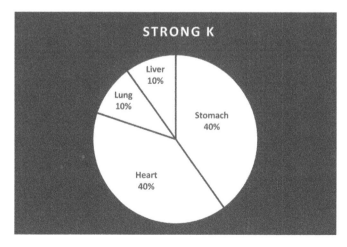

This domineering body system is very difficult to get ahead of in spiritual practice. The desire may be there, but the system goes everywhere and has no respect for other organs.

For that reason, this body system has many health issues if not maintained properly.

If it's not taken care of internally, this body system will interfere with people externally as well.

Help needs to come from Stomach and Heart food first so that the body can begin to function better.

Once the body system is stabilized by Heart and Stomach food, then you can add in food from other areas if needed.

Avoid all Kidney food at all costs no matter how good it looks or tastes. Wanting Kidney food is an auto-pilot habit that must be overcome.

Food to Stabilize **Strong Kidney-Kidney**

Recommended food intake percentages:

1) 60% Stomach food, 40% Heart food until stabilized.

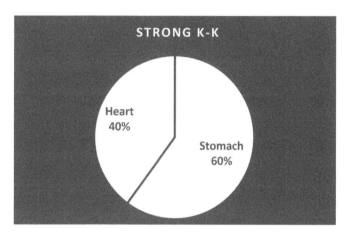

Also, try to take 7 days' vacation in Arizona—this will help your body discover what freedom means.

2) Then move to 50% Stomach food, 30% Heart food, 10% Lung food, 10% Liver food.

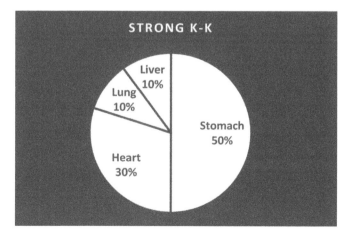

Kidney-Kidney

This is much more severe than a Strong Kidney. The body has no anchor system. It goes everywhere and nowhere. It just wants to flow and flow.

To make any meaningful progress in practice, the body must be stabilized by concentrating 3-4 times intensely on balancing Strong Kidney. It's crucial to maintain the body system.

This domineering Kidney body system can be extremely rude and negative, and it can also make it difficult for you to focus on a spiritual practice due to excess head spin caused by unstable Stomach. Stabilize this imbalance by taking Stomach and Heart food to reduce excess thinking and keep the body functioning better.

If not cared for properly, this body system will face many major health issues, resulting in visits to doctors and hospitals.

This body system will also interfere externally with another's energy field. And it doesn't know how to stop.

This body structure is only at ease with a person who has strong Stomach & Heart. Then it's a win/win situation. Both can share each other's energy and make each other whole and happy.

If you're suffering from Strong Kidney, how do you make significant progress in your practice? Move to a hot energy area like Arizona where you can dry your body system continuously. Above all, don't follow Kidney habits.

Stabilize this body system with Heart and Stomach food first, then you can move onto other areas.

Avoid Kidney food at all costs, as it will cause the system to flip back to the imbalanced way it was. The Kidney system doesn't know right or wrong or good or bad. Because the Kidney system is too strong, it wants to keep going Kidney's way. Kidney's way is to spin and spin in the pool of water.

Food to Stabilize **Strong Kidney-Heart**

Recommended food intake percentages:

60% Lung food, 20% Liver food, 20% Stomach food.

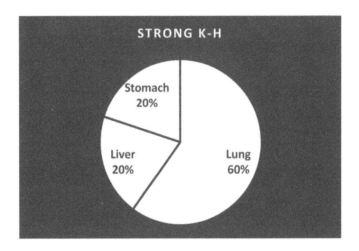

People with a Strong Kidney-Heart system are easily withdrawn. With weak Lung power, it's difficult for them to move forward. The first thing is to focus on Lung food, a lot of it. Avoid Kidney and Heart food at all costs if you are to make any meaningful progress on your journey.

Food to Stabilize **Strong Kidney-Liver**

Recommended food intake percentages:

40% Stomach food, 30% Heart food, 30% Lung food.

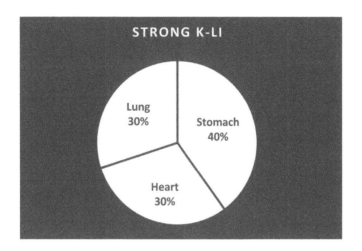

This body system is on non-stop video replay in your head. Until this body system becomes balanced, there's no way to progress.

This body system must secure Stomach food first, then move on to Heart and Lung foods.

Food to Stabilize **Strong Kidney-Lung**

Recommended food intake percentages:

50% Heart food, 30% Stomach food, 20% Liver food.

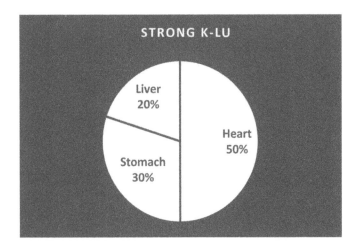

A person with this system is overly critical and judgmental. Due to weak Heart & Stomach support, progress will be delayed.

This body system must secure Heart and Stomach food.

Food to Stabilize **Strong Kidney-Stomach**

Recommended food intake percentages:

70% Heart food, 15% Lung food, 15% Liver food.

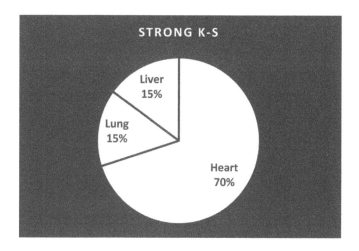

This body system is very weak in Heart. The most critical problem is that the body system itself extinguishes Heart energy continuously. No meaningful progress can be made without strong Heart and Lung support.

When Kidney energy is provided by the Universe, this will cause serious health issues. Adjust your current eating habits immediately.

Food to Stabilize **Strong Heart**

Recommended food intake percentages:

40% Lung food, 25% Kidney food, 20% Liver food, 15% stomach food. Consume Kidney and Stomach food together first, then move on to foods for the other organs.

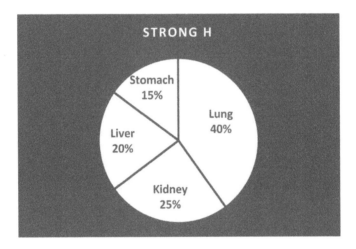

Strong Heart has a tendency to burn everything in the system both internally and externally. No meaningful progress can occur until there's enough support from the Lung and Kidney.

Food to Stabilize **Strong Heart-Kidney**

Recommended food intake percentages:

60% Lung food, 25% Stomach food, 15% Liver food.

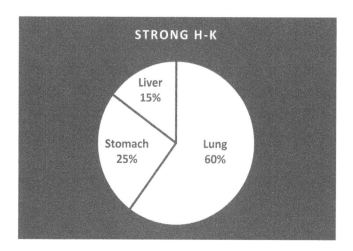

This body system has a tendency to make a person get caught in emotional rhythms, which makes it very difficult to progress.

See "Kidney-Heart."

Food to Stabilize **Strong Heart-Heart**

Recommended food intake percentages:

60% Kidney food and 40% Stomach food.

1. For first 3 months

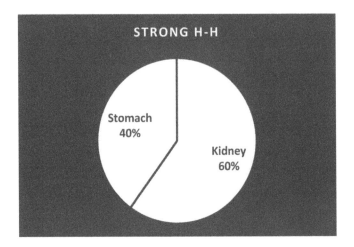

This body system is unstable. Living on the Seattle waterfront is highly recommended.

WHAT TO EAT AND WHAT NOT TO EAT

2. After 3 months

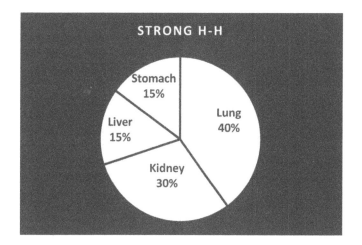

Go back to #1 if too tired and short breathing issues persist.

This body system wants to burn everything around it, including itself. This body structure makes it very difficult to be calm and centered.

Consuming seaweed and turnip soup daily is recommended to contain the internal fire from bursting.

One raw mid-size turnip pureed with ½ cup of milk will do wonders.

Food to Stabilize **Strong Heart-Liver**

Recommended food intake percentages:

60% Lung food, 20% Kidney food, 20% Stomach food.

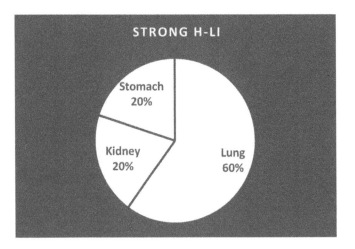

To make meaningful progress, much Lung food is needed. With strong support for the Lung, positive changes can begin to happen.

Food to Stabilize **Strong Heart-Lung**

Recommended food intake percentages:

30% Stomach food, 45% Liver food, 25% Kidney food.

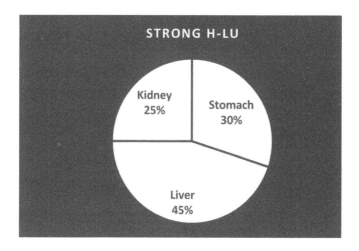

Consuming Liver food is extremely important in this case to gain compassion. However, this body system must first secure Stomach food before taking on Liver food.

With careful adjustments of food intake, fast progress is possible.

Food to Stabilize **Strong Heart-Stomach**

Recommended food intake percentages:

40% Lung food, 40% Kidney food, 20% Liver food

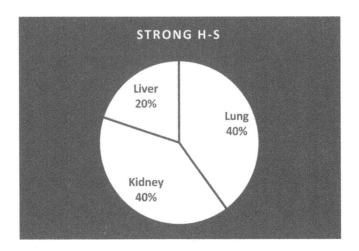

This body type has a weak defense system.

The desire is strong—you can almost taste it. But this body system can't withstand any long-term commitment due to its weak Lung and Kidney. With strong Lung and Kidney support, you will get closer to the goal. Otherwise, you'll go right back to the start.

Interlude Dialog: A Zen Master Talks to a Strong Heart-Stomach Zen Student

A Strong Heart-Stomach Zen student had a meeting with a Zen master, hoping to enter resident practice at the Zen center. He had already been on a Zen practice journey for some time.

Student: I'd like to study under you if you permit me. I am diligent, honest, and a hard worker. I'm in harmony with all people.

Zen Master: What version would you like to hear this time?

Student: What do you mean? *(He was puzzled)*

Zen master: What do you want to hear from me this time?

Student: ??? This is not first time?

Zen master: …. The same questions have been asked over many lifetimes.

Student: It means that I have not made any improvement since then?

Zen master: (warm smile)

Student: I thought I was good at deceiving people.

Zen master: You should know that deceiving someone is deceiving yourself. It damages you more than others.

Student: I will work on that this time. Will you take me as your student.

Zen master: To add more heavy-duty karma?

Student: No. I will study under you to work on it.

Zen master: Can you do volunteer work for three years?

Student: Yes. I will do whatever you want me to do here.

Zen master: I am thinking of an elderly adult care facility for three years without pay.

Student: I want to study under you.

Zen master: ....

Student: I am talking about here with you.

Zen master: I know what you mean. That's my recommendation. To provide their comfort without taking anything from them emotionally or financially. Then perhaps there will be a room for you here.

Student: How often?

Zen master: Every day.

Many conversations later, the student agreed upon the Zen master's recommendation. He tried volunteering for a few days and came back.

Student: That's not my area of expertise.

Zen master: What is your expertise?

Student: I can contribute so much here at the center and be useful to you. I have a degree in marketing and have done good jobs for the previous teacher.

Zen master: Well... I don't look for your talents to help me or my center, nor your expertise. Your expertise hinders your practice. When you can rest your expertise and find your real determination to practice, then your practice will begin.

I do not teach how to lick the outside of the watermelon. I teach how to go directly into the core of the watermelon.

Student: That is why I am here. Your preciseness.

Zen master: You have been on this upside-down path for a long time. You don't want to give up the upside-down thinking. My offer still stands. Once you complete three years volunteering, you will have a room here.

Student: Is there any other way?

Zen master: No. That might give you a chance to get back to yourself.

Food to Stabilize **Strong Liver**

Recommended food intake percentages:

30% Stomach food, 30% Lung food, 30% Heart food, 10% Kidney food. Consume Stomach and Heart food together first, then move on to foods for the other organs.

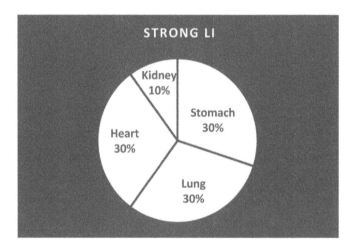

This body system often manifests as a person being highly intellectual, but weak in physical reality.

This body system is not movable. Even with adjustments, this body system resists change. One must make a deliberate daily effort to create some movement. That itself is practice for this body system. It's slow to start, but once it starts to run, it will go all the way.

Food to Stabilize **Strong Liver-Kidney**

Recommended food intake percentages:

50% Stomach food, 25% Heart food, 25% Lung food.

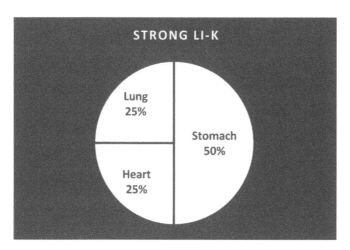

A person with this body system may appear weak in physical reality, but actually has great physical and mental endurance.

This body system must secure stomach food first.

Food to Stabilize **Strong Liver-Heart**

Recommended food intake percentages:

60% Lung food, 20% Stomach food, 20% Kidney food.

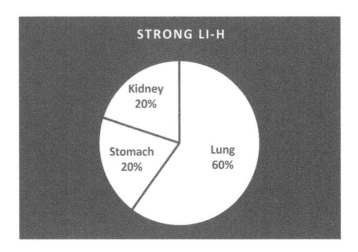

This body system needs to focus on intaking strong Lung energy in order to make significant progress forward.

See "Heart-Liver."

Food to stabilize **Strong Liver-Liver**

Recommended food intake percentages:

30% Stomach food, 30% Lung food, 25% Heart food, 15% Kidney food.

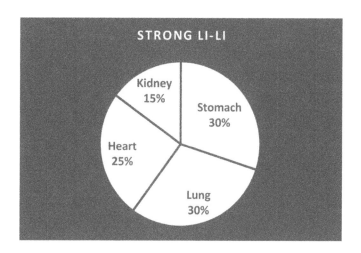

It is very difficult for this body type to become balanced quickly. It will take time and dedication. Consider intaking extra snacks between (or with) meals for extra support from Lung, Stomach, and Heart food.

This body system must secure Stomach food first.

See "Strong Liver."

Food to Stabilize **Strong Liver-Lung**

Recommended food intake percentages:

55% Heart food, 30% Stomach food, 15% Kidney food.

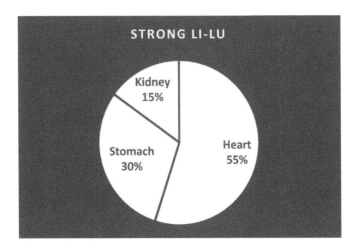

This body system is mentally ahead of the game. But without support from Heart and Stomach, it can't see anything ahead.

In order to stabilize this body system, first secure Stomach food and then Heart food.

Food to Stabilize **Strong Liver-Stomach**

Recommended food intake percentages:

35% Lung food, 35% Kidney food, 30% Heart food.

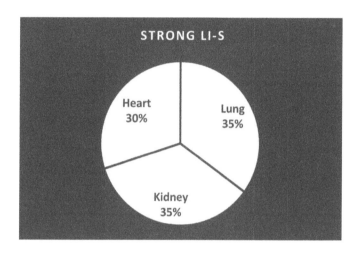

With this body system, progress will be fruitless until all other organ support is in place.

Food to Stabilize **Strong Lung**

Recommended food intake percentages:

35% Stomach foods, 25% Heart foods, 25% Liver foods, 15% Kidney foods. Consume Stomach and Kidney food first, then add in Heart and Liver foods in that order.

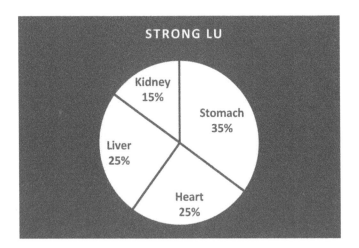

Food to Stabilize **Strong Lung-Kidney**

Recommended food intake percentages:

45% Heart food, 35% Stomach food, 20% Liver food.

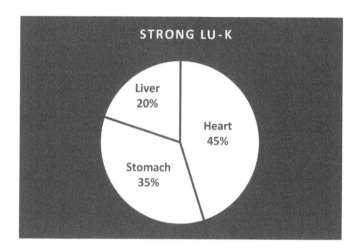

People with this body system tend to be very impatient, but with a proper change in eating habits, they will calm down and will see things more clearly.

This body system must secure Stomach and Heart food first.

See "Strong Kidney-Lung."

Food to Stabilize **Strong Lung-Heart**

Recommended food intake percentages:

60% Liver food, 25% Stomach food, 15% Kidney food.

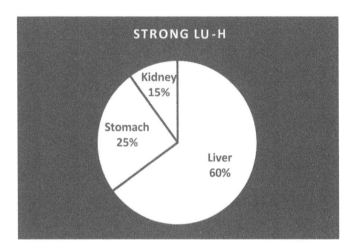

In this instance, it's very important to build up the Liver system. After that, it's very easy to make progress.

This body system must secure Stomach food before taking on Liver food.

Interlude Dialog: A Zen Master Talks to a Strong Lung-Heart Zen Student

A future Zen practitioner went to see a well-known Zen master and expressed his desire to learn Zen.

Zen master: Why Zen?

Student: Words are not Zen. Reading and chanting are not Zen. I would like to practice with someone with awakened eyes to train me to be a real human being.

Zen master: Where have you been?

Student: Everywhere and nowhere.

Zen master: Hmm. It's going to be a tough and difficult road to be a real human being.

Student: I've tried on my own. I do not see any other option but this.

Zen master: What about your family?

Student: Pain and suffering without a light at the end of the tunnel. No thanks. And I took care of all my responsibilities to them as much as I could. So, no one should come after me. I don't have any reason to go back to them. This is my journey. I must be on it.

Zen master: What are your strong wants and desires in life?

Student: To learn and make the journey to realize my existence on this earth. I know there's a reason. I need to find it and complete it.

Zen master: What makes you think there's something that needs to be done?

Student: I've always known. But didn't care to know. It was a fantastic life and meaningless life. I was soaked in this external life until recently.

Zen master: So, what will you do when those habits come to bite you?

Student: Yes, the memories will come visit me as visitors passing through. But they can't move me.

After much talking and walking together, the master accepted the student with some rules in place. If he violated any Zen center rules or any aspect of his teaching, the student would have to leave. The student agreed.

Food to Stabilize **Strong Lung-Liver**

Recommended food intake percentages:

50% Heart food, 35% Stomach food, 15% Kidney food.

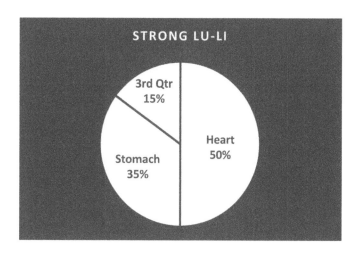

This body system must secure the Stomach first. Once the body system has reached an adequate and balanced level, it will result in improved views and relationships with others.

See "Liver-Lung."

Food to Stabilize **Strong Lung-Lung**

Recommended food intake percentages:

1) 50% Heart food, 50% Kidney food for first 3 months.

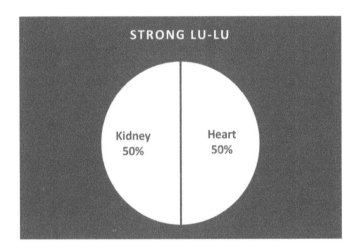

This is a very volatile body system.

2) After 3 months, modify intake as follows:

25% Stomach food, 30% Heart food, 30% Kidney food, 15% Liver food. (Adding daily ginseng extract is also recommended.)

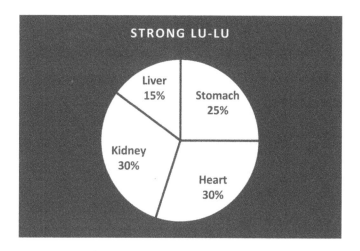

If health issues arise from time to time, go back to #1 (Heart food 50% & Kidney food 50%). Go back and forth as needed.

The most delicate and volatile body system is strong Lung or strong Lung-Lung. Because there aren't many people with these body systems in the population, not a lot of research has been done, and there are no solid treatments available. Many people with these body structures die prematurely if not properly taken care of.

It's important to intake Kidney & Heart food for the first three months. When the body finds some breathing room, then add Stomach food, followed finally by Liver food.

If this body system consumes too much Liver food before stabilizing the Stomach, the systems can go into shock or become sick due to influx Liver energy. The Stomach can't handle it. For that reason, many people with this body structure tend to not take much-needed Liver food, as they've already had bad experiences with it. But the Liver food is truly needed—you just first have to make sure your Stomach is strong enough to handle it.

This body structure is delicate and very difficult to care for or to maintain. For the health and longevity of this body structure, we highly recommend a plant-based diet. Animal or fish diets will cause this body serious health damage and possibly result in an early earthly departure.

Because this body structure is so delicate and complicated, we choose to ignore it—but the condition will continue until we address it. Once we understand this system, and we can see how it functions, it will allow us to continue our journey happily, and not experience a premature death.

Having a strong virtue account is recommended. (See page 110.)

We also recommend Susin Ogapy Royal. This extract dissolves into the body system without causing any issues. It can be expensive for some, but it's worth it when one considers what it does to help this body system. Other inexpensive items can't deliver in the same way that Susin Ogapy Royal can. One problem is there's no direct purchase available currently. Find Koreans to help you with purchase. The author has no ties to them whatsoever and will not benefit from purchases. www.susinogapy.com

Food to Stabilize **Strong Lung-Stomach**

Recommended food intake percentages:

40% Liver food, 40% Heart food, 20% Kidney food.

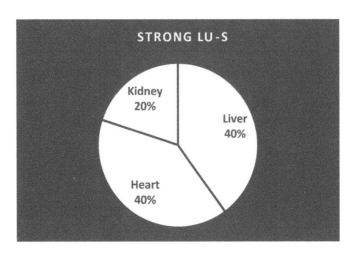

People with this body system often have weak Liver power and a lack of circulation. They can be controlling, quick to blame others, and easily angered.

To make just the right adjustment to this body structure will take time and require patience and temperance.

Food as medicine: Combine 1 can clam/clam juice, ½ cup corn, ½ cup chopped zucchini, ½ cup chopped mushroom, 8 oz water, salt, or soy sauce into a pot. Once boiled, add 2 eggs & 1 chopped or sliced Granny Smith Apple.

Food to Stabilize **Strong Stomach**

Recommended food intake percentages:

40% Kidney food, 20% Liver food, 20% Lung food, 20% Heart food. Consume Kidney and Heart food together first, then move on to foods for the other organs.

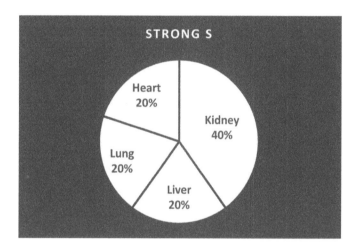

The most common problems found with this body structure include a lack of circulation and Kidney issues. Once a person begins this new diet, their body will begin to have more movement and flow within it.

Food to Stabilize **Strong Stomach-Kidney**

Recommended food intake percentages:

50% Heart food, 25% Lung food, 25% Liver.

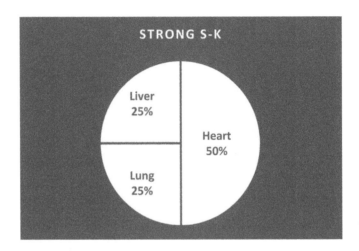

This body system continues to extinguish Heart energy, dampening it down into darkness.

See "Strong Kidney-Stomach."

Food to Stabilize **Strong Stomach-Heart**

Recommended food intake percentages:

40% Kidney food, 40% Lung food, 20% Liver food.

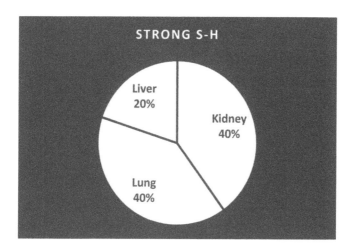

People with this body structure may collapse easily due to not enough Lung and Kidney power.

See "Strong Heart-Stomach."

Food to Stabilize **Strong Stomach-Liver**

Recommended food intake percentages:

35% Kidney food, 35% Heart food, 30% Lung food.

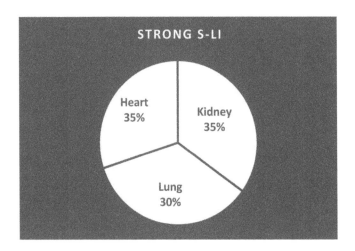

A person with this particular body structure can almost taste enlightenment, but without extra help from Lung, Kidney, and Heart energy, they will be delayed in getting it.

See "Strong Liver-Stomach."

Food to Stabilize **Strong Stomach-Lung**

Recommended food intake percentages:

40% Liver food, 40% Heart food, 20% Kidney food.

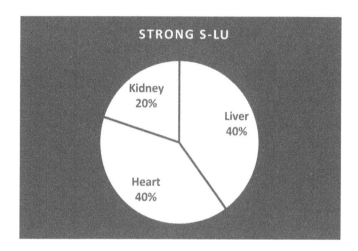

People with this body system can be very focused on collecting and keeping things in control. They're quick to blame others and get angry, and they have a hard time. They're also likely to have skin issues.

See "Strong Lung-Stomach."

Food to Stabilize **Strong Stomach-Stomach.**

Recommended food intake percentages:

1) 50% Kidney food, 50% Heart food for first three months.

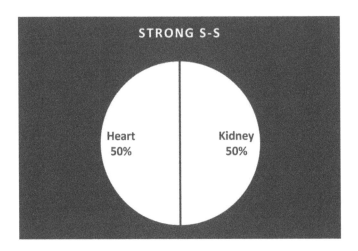

People with this particular body structure have a very difficult time creating space within themselves for a free flow of energy. But given enough time and effort, it can be done.

2) 3 months later

30% Kidney food, 30% Lung food, 20% Heart food, 20% Liver food.

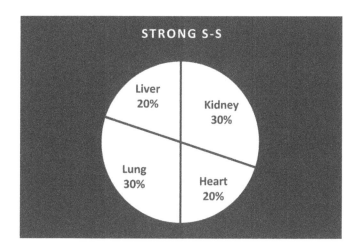

When you need to eat between meals, make sure it's 50% Kidney food and 50% Heart food. Avoid all Stomach food.

Go back to #1 (50% Kidney and 50% Heart) if the need arises.

Food as daily medicine: Combine 1 cup seaweed, ¼ cup kelp, 20 oz water, 1/2 cup corn, black pepper, ground pepper, salt, or soy sauce. Once boiled, reduce heat to medium-low for 20 mins.

Chapter 2

Reclaiming Ownership

Charity

We can donate to anyone or any organization. Our donations should be clean and sincere offerings, and can include food, clothing, medicine, talent, lodging, money, and good deeds. Whatever we can offer to those in need is considered charity.

Those who give charity will receive many blessings in return, including a possible spiritual upgrade. However, the key to true charity is that it must be offered without condition, and without expecting anything in return. Giving must be done with an empty and pure mind. Donations must be offered freely, without doubt, grumbling, or calculation of any kind. Once we've accomplished this act of giving, we must immediately let it go, and not cling to any idea of how great and kind and charitable we are. If we wish to be recognized for the deed, that's the ego talking. So, we do our giving as discreetly as possible, without fanfare. We give and let go.

We have already received a blessing in the act itself. The way of giving offers a gift to the giver as well.

If we find ourselves on the receiving end of a gift or a donation, whatever we're given, no matter how humble, it is to be received with sincere appreciation. There is no judging or weighing of that gift. By accepting gifts with whole sincerity, we are allowing the other person to fill their virtue account as we fill our own. In essence, giver and receiver are blessing each other in exchange.

It's in our benefit to help others. Doing charity helps us to release poisons within us. What do we want more for?

We may not realize it, but it's a thief's habit to want more. Also, that's the ego's way. Our ego has no shame in it. Our ego system bounds us so tightly, making sure we stay deeply rooted in the physical realm.

The same holds true for our strong karma—when we blindly follow karma, we are guaranteeing we will remain stuck here, bound forever to the earthly realm.

If instead of following karma, we learn to practice the six Prajna Paramitas to purify the way, we can avoid being earthly bound.

Six Prajna Paramitas:

Charity
Morality
Patience
Devotion
Meditation
Wisdom

Karma

What's karma?

Karma is something we have done in the past that carries repercussions for us. It is also a pattern of repeating habits over and over.

When does karma stop?

It goes on until *we* stop. Self-retrospection helps to identify what we are doing and can also help us decide whether to continue these actions. However, if a domineering organ takes over, we are no longer in control, and our habits and karma make all the decisions. It is very important to have a balanced body system so that every organ system has a vote.

Awareness is key. When we realize there is no benefit in continuing a certain habit, we can become the real owner of our actions and stop doing it. Sometimes this is easy—sometimes not so easy.

Sometimes we may try to change, only to fall back into old habits. When we do certain habits repeatedly, they become like second nature to us. We may even think these habits are the real us.

Once we no longer follow habits/karma, we will no longer be in a rat race. That will make our habit pause and wonder what just happened.

It's so important to have a virtue account—a reservoir of good energy that you've created through good deeds. This virtue account helps us to see better and make corrections as we want to. Without it, we may think we're going somewhere, but the truth is we're just going in circles without making any progress. Our virtue account helps us to stay the course.

Can I choose what I want to be in my next life? Yes. But only if we are free of debts and obligations and know how to connect the dots. If not, we may dream about it, but we may still be under karma's rule. For example, if we had debt with someone and that didn't get paid off whatever reason, that karma will maintain a strong pull on us. So, no matter what we want to be, karma will not let this happen until the debt is paid in full.

We need to work on shedding our heavy karma so we will have freedom to plan and choose who we want to be and how we want to live.

Sincere prayers and virtue accounts will also help us to shed karma that we've been carrying. Adding the Shurangama Sutra will accelerate this process.

This sutra is not well known to general Buddhist practitioners, but serious Zen practitioners should memorize it by heart. It's that important on our Zen journey.

The following is a shorter version of a three-page long sutra. A few pristine mountain Zen retreats make it a prerequisite for all monks to memorize the sutra before they will consider accepting them for a three-month retreat.

This sutra is called the secret Shurangama sutra. Reciting it invokes a bright light that lifts the dark energies within us, around us, to remove barriers, and breaks away many layers and chains of karma.

Shurangama Sutra

Om anale anale visade visade vira vjra-dhare,
Bandha bandhani, vajra-pani phat! Hum trum phat! Svaha.

Continue to repeat. Chant daily and whenever possible.

The Virtue Account

What is the virtue account?

When we provide kind deeds, talents, or monetary donations to churches, temples, organizations, disaster events, and people who need our help, the resulting positive energy will go into our virtue account.

Having a sufficient virtue account in place is highly recommended for myriad reasons. Most importantly, we need enough virtue account in place for us to reach our destination.

How does it work?

Let's say we are in trouble and hoping for someone to help us. With no virtue account, people would just pass us by. Their instinct tells them to avoid us, to not get involved. Often, helping someone with no virtue account, regrettable outcomes occur.

With a strong virtue account in place, on the other hand, if we are in trouble, someone will notice us and be glad to assist us. In a life-and-death situation, having a virtue account can make a huge difference.

The other positive aspect is that when we have done enough good deeds or given enough donations to fill up our virtue account, we finally get answers to questions that have been spinning in our heads for a long time.

Experience it!

Live as Owner

Some people are very close to having complete ownership of their lives physically, mentally, and spiritually. They only need a slight change to become the true master of themselves and complete their journey.

Others of us are trying to be the owner, but something is not quite connecting, and we are unable to become the person we want to be. For instance, someone might have a strong logical and intellectual understanding of the path they want to take, but because they are spiritually weak, they are unable to walk down that path. In this case, the person must pay attention to their own body structure and fill in the missing links to reach a stable level. Then their journey will improve, and they will have a better chance of establishing full ownership.

Some of us are not in the owner's shoes at all. Since there's no real owner in sight, their habits are in charge and are dictating everything in their daily lives. Because it is not the habits' function to care for the owner's well-being, this creates endless suffering. These habits will be repeated over and over.

Some people wonder: if it's our habits that are doing things, why is it still our responsibility?

The answer is that we give permission to our habits to carry on. On their own, habits don't have the capacity to be the owner— they can only copy other people's ideas and experiences. But another person's path might not be the right one for us.

Without balancing our body system first, habits will continue to cause further damage. Close the gap and become the true owner! Your habits want their way and may say, *don't close gap*. But it should be our decision, not theirs. We must decide for ourselves what we want to do or be.

Be the Owner

As the owner, it is our responsibility to carry the load, not the habit's. Remember, our habits are not true to us, and they can't carry out our responsibility as owners. Whatever habits are created, it's our responsibility. Why is that? Because we allowed them to by neglecting to do our part. Whenever habits are created, they are recorded and stored in our DNA.

It doesn't even matter if we don't remember what we did—we still bear responsibility for every single one of our actions, even if they were initiated by our habits. Some time ago, a man entered a "not guilty" plea for a murder because he didn't remember ever doing it. But the act was recorded, and a witness provided details. How could he not remember what he did? It's a scary thing, isn't it? The court found him guilty and sent him to jail.

It's important to build up our body system strong so that we can be better owners, and not end up being used by another person or thing. If we are pushed around internally by a domineering system, we will be pushed around in our external life, too.

Nobody has ownership of our body but us. Be the owner, show the proof of ownership, and claim it.

For some, becoming the true owner may be an easy process. For some, it's a difficult process and takes time. But it will be worth it.

Whatever stage we are in, until we become the true owner, the master of our body system, there's no true freedom. Until then, our confusion, misunderstanding, pain, and suffering will continue.

If we are indeed the owner, be firm. Remember, we are responsible for our own upgrades. To do that correctly, we must have a strong balanced body system now and continual basis. Without a strong support from the body system, we can't go where we need to go or to be. Can an eagle fly with broken wings?

We do not just live one life. Rather, it is a continuation: one life and then the next. Unless we want to repeat our lives over and over, claim ownership fully.

False vs. Genuine

We need to know the difference between the real us and the false us. In reality, the difference is less than paper-thin.

The fake part of us does not follow the way of principle and virtue, and it refuses to accept the true self as owner. We must exercise our rights as owners.

Our real selves are not influenced by external ideas. But our false selves can get easily caught up in unproven mental mumbo jumbo, which they're convinced is real. Our false selves can make something look very appetizing even though there's nothing of substance within it. We need to not be influenced by these kinds of empty, pretty packages.

Often, we make mistakes hoping that something is there when it's really not. Such wishes vanish into thin air. Just because we hope something is real does not make it real.

And don't get confused and fight for the wrong side, okay? Make sure that we are not deceived into believing that our habits are in charge.

One way to test whether it is our real or false self is that the real us has true wisdom, while the false side of us relies on smartness and baseless claims. Our false self has no deep-rooted foundations.

Whatever comes through organs and senses are functions. This functionality is not the real us. It's part of us and of our body's function, but no matter how much we want to believe in it, it is not the full and complete us.

Can our stomach, lung, liver, kidney, or heart be the real you? What about the feeling that is associated with those organs? Can they be the real us?

Is a domineering organ that thinks it's in charge the real us?

When we are driving a car, who is the legal owner of the car? Who pays for car payment and regular maintenance? It's not the engine, or the oil, water, tires, gas, or brake pad—it's us! We get the idea, right?

These may be parts of us, but they are not the true owners. So why are we following them when it comes to spiritual matters?

If some of us are still confused, practice and practice. This will help us find answers and become our genuine Self.

Genuine does not have to convince anyone. The True Self can just be.

The False Owner

A woman named Sue lived in a beautiful condo. She loved the place, but there was one problem: limited parking spaces. Since Sue had two cars, she had to purchase an extra parking space, which was recorded in the deed.

During her residence there, she had to be someplace else for three months for work. Except for the weekends.

However, when her work was completed and she returned to the condo full time, her extra parking space had been taken by someone with the same car.

Sue left notes on the car windshield, but it didn't work. Towing warnings didn't work, either. She knocked on the door of the parking space thief's unit and talked to them, but they didn't care. As far as they were concerned, the space was vacant when they moved in, and therefore it was theirs to take. Sue explained her situation and showed the thief the deed, but they still didn't care. This went on for months.

On a rainy Friday night after work, Sue couldn't find anywhere to park. All the visitors' parking spaces were taken. Finally, she'd had enough. She'd been hoping for a peaceful way to solve the problem, but it seemed it was never going to end in a peaceful way. Sue had to exercise her rights as the space owner.

Sue called a towing company. She had to show the proof of ownership of the parking space before the towing could took place.

The thief's car was towed away. Sue's parking space was hers once more.

A vacant space does not mean it has no owner.

The problem should have ended there. But on Monday morning, the space taker wanted to go to work but discovered their car had been towed. They knocked on Sue's door and complained—how dare she call the towing company and tow her car! They didn't have the money to get the car out of storage, and felt Sue was being insensitive to their needs.

The situation didn't have to go that far. All the person had to do was simply vacate the parking space they didn't own, and there would have been no further trouble. It would have been that simple. But instead, they ignored Sue's ample warnings and chose to be a bully instead. It cost them several hundred dollars.

It didn't end there. A few days later, they knocked on Sue's door again saying Sue must pay their towing bill since she was one who called the towing company. Sue reminded them that she had given them more than enough time to correct their mistakes, and that she had no responsibility for paying the towing bill. She informed them she was going to report the whole incident to their landlord and agency.

After that she didn't have to deal with this person on any other issues.

Sue had to exercise her rights as the owner. We can do the same and exercise our rights to be 100% owner of our bodies and our lives.

Chapter 3

Preparation for Serious Practitioners

Self-Prayers

Pray sincerely, deep within.

To remove or release some of things in the air, recite the following prayer.

"I repent for all wrongs and harmful deeds ever committed by me, knowingly and unknowingly, on account of my ignorance, greed, and anger, through my body, my thoughts, and my will, with or without my realizing them. Today, I repent for it all." (After this, we can add what else we want to say—but make no deals, no negotiations and no begging.) Finally, recite "Om sal bah mot jah motji sah dah yah sah bah hah" three times.

We commit many wrongdoings that we are not aware of when we are trapped by ignorance. When we walk on grass or pavement, we don't see that there are other things alive also taking walks, and we may bring them harm without even realizing it. We just walk without any consideration for them. For instance, there may be little bugs out there, but because we couldn't see them, we stepped on them and killed them without any remorse. But as far as we know, these insects had feelings and were aware of being killed.

The above prayer will cover not only our harmful deeds we were aware of, but also those deeds that we committed without knowing. We've done many things in life unknowingly without considering the consequences. Acknowledging this through prayer helps to release us of this karma, as long as we are sincere.

After this, we can pray to ourselves for what we truly want. We can communicate our desires with much more clarity, and we can reach deep within.

1. Indicate what you're praying for, and why. Be precise.

2. Have a specific plan for what you promise to do once the prayer is answered.

3. Make sure you keep your promises once your prayers have been realized.

If we reach deep within and connect to our True Essence, the Universe will record our prayers, and one way or another, they will be answered.

Preparing for Enlightenment

A long time ago, all of us were endowed with a perfect body system. But along the way, we chose to follow certain paths, chasing our desires and creating negative habits, and we kept doing this over and over until we became imbalanced and found ourselves further and further away from the True Self.

Now, so much time has passed, we don't even remember we once had this perfect system.

To return to a better body system, we must replenish the areas in ourselves that now are lacking.

We must work to achieve this, so we can make our body function better and build a strong foundation that can stand any wind, rain, or snowstorms along the way. First, we must stop following the habits that created imbalance in the body system.

When we are embarking on a spiritual journey to reach our True Essence/Buddhahood, we must make sure not to bring our preconceived notions about what this journey will involve.

Our faith in the journey is a very important one. But in order to arrive at our destination, we must make sure our body system can support our journey.

Some people are fully equipped to do that, but most people are held back by wrong ideas and habits.

We will only go as far on our journey as our body's capacity allows. Yes, our will is much stronger than a body system, but without the right mind and proper support from a fully functional body, we can't make it through to the end.

If we choose to ignore the lack in our body system, our path to enlightenment will be off to a bad start. What will happen may not be what we want. Prep work is required.

With the right mind, we can learn to take care of our body system now rather than later. Someday, we must learn to be the master of our body system, so it might as well be now.

We might assume that some people arrived at their destination without learning to master their body system first. But what we must consider is how long these people were actually preparing, whether it seems that way or not. On extremely rare occasions, a special person with a strong will may overcome their body's disharmony with apparent ease, but even then, it is likely they've received help from higher places.

Most of us remain caught in a dysfunctional system and can't balance our body as easily as the rare special person can.

When our body is in serious disharmony, are we able to demand that it function as normal? It's impossible. We tell ourselves that we are better than this, but that thought is useless to our sick body. We need to take care of ourselves first.

For example, if someone with a Strong Lung tells someone with no lung power to do what a Strong Lung person does, it can't be done. (Conversely, the Strong-Lung person can't be flexible or soft as a Weak-Lung person.) The point is, if we tell someone with a different body structure, "Mind over matter," this person would likely fall into depression. A person with weak lungs probably has a strong Heart-Kidney, Kidney-Heart, Heart-Heart, or Heart-Stomach—body systems that continue to weaken their Lung system.

The only solution is for this person to eat Lung food until their body system is stabilized. Then the problem will disappear rather quickly, and the person will no longer be weak like before. In fact, that person will no longer be the same person as before.

It is crucial to take care of a situation like this first. If we don't learn our body structure, our suffering will continue for years.

Eventually, we must fix this problem. No one can fix it for us. It's up to us. To reach the destination, we must make our body suitable for the journey.

When the body becomes ill or a problem arises, no matter how big the problem is, don't try to fix the symptoms. As owner of body, first try to fill the weakest organs. That is the shortest and most effective way. In most cases, all other issues subside.

But if we are not the owner, we will look for ways to compensate for our weaker organs while mistakenly supporting the one organ causing the issue. This will only prolong the process and guarantee that we will continue to suffer.

Knowing that our body, mind, and spirit must be one with us allows us to make solid, steady progress on this journey. If any part of the three is missing, our journey will continue, but we will be delayed reaching the destination until all three operate as one.

Pay Debts Off

When it comes to monetary debts, paying them off will give us a certain freedom from their burden. Don't delay paying them off.

Due dates can vary. Some debts are due now. Some can be paid later. It's always wise to pay them off as soon as we can. Delaying paying them off can result in a heavy weight on our shoulders that we're forced to carry on our journey. Sometimes, we can't even take a step. Imagine: we are in middle of deep meditation, and the debt collector comes.

There are also nonmonetary debts and burdens, such as promises, lies, misunderstandings, regrettable fights, and all sorts of other ways we may cause harm to people, with or without any intention of repenting or apologizing.

In meditation, pray for the resolution of these non-monetary debts until they are no longer in our thoughts.

It's easier to be honest with our feelings when the person is not in front of us.

Recite a silent prayer and repent.

Be honest and sincere. Say how sorry we are. The deeds were made in our ignorance. Ask them to forgive us for our ignorant deeds. Pray for them and wish them happiness throughout their lives.

We can say whatever we want to say, as long as it's said with sincerity. Whoever we harmed that we want to direct our prayers towards, the prayers will be delivered to them. Pray for them until they are no longer in our thoughts. We will have more space and freedom from it.

Pay monetary & nonmonetary debts off and be free from them. No more notices, no more reminders, no more demands, no more stress.

It's great to be debt-free. It gives us a clear conscience so we can move forward with our journey.

Now that that's out of our hair, we can take time to get to know ourselves. It will be much easier than before. With no agenda, we can just take time to be with ourselves, to listen, yet without clinging to our stories— no matter how great, sad, painful, and loving they might be. Just allow it all to flow out of our system.

Once all stories and events have flowed out of our system, we can hear voices deep within us. These are the soft and gentle words that can lead us to the wisdom pond. Also, we will discover that we are buddhas. Believe it. Trust it.

Do not worship anything external. Turn within and shine the light on the sacred holiness deep inside us. This is our True Self.

Awareness

What's awareness?

It's like having a security system for our home or business. The security system records everything. If something is approaching or a movement is detected, the system gives us an alert. We investigate the alert, and if we realize it's harmless, or something we recognize to be safe, we dismiss the alerts. But if something is actually wrong like a break-in, a red alert is issued, and the police are called to investigate.

We have a fantastic awareness system. It gives us an alert if there's any unusual activity in our sensory fields, like an intruder. We then investigate and decide if it is safe, or if we need to act.

If it is indeed an intruder, we can give the intruder a warning. If the intruder continues to invade, then we take strong measures to remove them.

The same thing happens in our built-in system. If the owner is not in sight, something else is in charge, like our habits, our karma, or a domineering organ. Sometimes, these will do an OK job watching the security system, but other times they will join up with the thief.

Who is watching our security camera system? We must be sure.

Practicing awareness means that we must always be present as a true owner.

We don't give someone or something else the power to look after us because we prefer to go on vacation from awareness. It's an extremely dangerous game, especially for Zen practitioners. Someone or something could take over the system and lock us out.

Be present and stay aware!

Often, we are confused by our habits masquerading as the true us. Another usual suspect is a domineering organ within our system. It only looks after it and its benefit.

That game could go on and on.

What if an alert was issued, but there's no owner in sight? Instead, someone was watching the security camera and deleted the scene and let the intruder in. They are working together to steal or harm the place, and they can easily do it since the recording was deleted by the watcher. We know something was deleted but don't know what.

True ownership must be established for Zen practitioners. Otherwise, these lies, pretenses, and confusions can go on until we realize or discover them. We must awaken from self-deception.

This built-in system of awareness is in every living being. Some have it less, some have it more, and some have a highly developed sense of awareness.

Even if our body system blocks everything and is too full to function, our awareness continues to record. When we reflect through meditation, we will see everything that happened, even if we thought its recollection had been erased. But it is wise to remove all the extra stuff that we don't need so our awareness can function better for us.

To be a true owner and progressing practitioner, build a strong virtue account. That will help us reclaim true ownership sooner rather than later.

The awareness must serve the true owner. With that, we can make the journey worthwhile.

Koan

What is a koan?

It is a riddle used in Zen Buddhism to demonstrate the inadequacy of logical reasoning and provoke enlightenment.

The greatest Koan arises from within us—a fundamental question that we must resolve.

"What is it?"

"Who am I?"

"Why am I here?"

"Why this suffering?"

"What am I?" And so on.

The Koan cuts off all other busy thoughts.

Every day, during all the things we do—sleeping, talking, eating, working, shopping, driving—we must continue to work on our koan. Our koan must be present in all things. It manifests in every function. *What is this?* Something present, knowing and watching.

What is this?

That's the question that we need to meditate on. We may get it quickly, or it may take a long time, depending on each person.

Chanting

Along with Koan-practice, some may find chanting soothing. Chanting can also help us to achieve a deep Samadhi—the Buddhist term for a deep meditative state or non-dualistic state of consciousness.

Chanting cuts off our busy minds and sheds some of our heavy karma.

Some practitioners prefer to chant rather than just sitting in the meditation hall. Because it's short and powerful, they can continue to chant day and night—even as they sleep. Some have been awakened by chanting.

Two popular examples of chanting:

Guan Yin Bodhisattva = Kwan Se Um Bo Sal

Amitabha = Ah-mi-tah-bul

When chanting their names, Kwan Se Um Bo Sal and Ah-mi-tah-bul may appear in many different forms to save sentient beings and to help practitioners on their journey.

Guan Yin Bodhisattva: Kwan Se Um Bo Sal oversees this earth. She wants to put an end to all suffering and make sure that all sentient beings make it home safely until end of the time.

> Kwan se um bo sal
> Kwan se um bo sal
> Kwan se um bo sal... (Continue to Repeat)

Amitabha Buddha resides in one of the heavens. According to Buddhist text, there are many heavens. If we chant Ah-mi-tah-bul, we not only get blessings in this lifetime but in the afterlife as well when we get invited to Amitabha's heaven.

> Na moo ah mi tah bul
> Na moo ah mi tah bul
> Na moo ah mi tah bul

> Continue to repeat. Chant daily and whenever possible.

What to Avoid

Our body is the vessel to our destination.

When we are seriously going into in depth practice and trying to discover who we really are—our True Self—it is crucial our body is a healthy vessel that can support this journey. We must be very careful what to eat and what not to eat for the optimum result.

Eat clean food that does not block our energy system, or trigger imbalances.

Our awareness must be on the here and now.

Our eyes must be open and stay focused on the journey.

As we progress along the path, our six senses will purify and upgrade as our practice gets stronger. Don't follow any distractions that result through our six senses experiencing phenomena. Our senses are just doing their thing—what they experience is not worth following or becoming attached to. Best to acknowledge these experiences and let them go. Be empty minded about it.

We have walked through those doors billions and billions of times before, only to gain nothing more than pain and suffering, habits and karma. We should know by now that ignorance leads us to a state of suffering and confusion brought on by the three poisons of greed, anger, and ignorance. Let go. Focus on the breath.

As we continue down the path to enlightenment, we come face to face with many things—great things, fantastic things, wondrous places, not so wondrous places. Let it all go.

Everything that we experience in this life is conditional—it's empty, not solid. It's not to be feared, followed, clicked, or joined with. Only acknowledge it and let go. If we are focused on the breath, it will disappear in no time.

How Food's Energy and Traits Can Transfer to Us

Why is avoiding certain food so important on this journey?

Every food contains energy, as well as certain traits. By consuming them, the energy and traits will transfer to our body system. This affects how we view things. If we are heavy on a certain energy, we see things through its eyes. We may or may not be aware of what's happening. We mistakenly assume that this is our own thinking and our own desires. Some foods are good for us, some interfere with us, some make us sexually aroused, some make us angry, some make us comfortable, some give us a variety of experiences. When we behave a certain way, is that us or is that the food we've been eating? We need to know for sure.

While on this journey, if we have an urge to eat steak and lobster for dinner, we can just taste it in our mouth—but we are in trouble if we follow through and actually eat it.

This desire might be coming from memories in us that need to play out, or it could be something triggering us to send us off track.

If we never had it, there's no mouthwatering taste to remember—no memory to remind us. It might just be a thought passing through our system that needs to be released. If we simply acknowledge it and let go, it's out of our system for good.

Steak and Lobster?

When do we eat steak and lobster? Special occasions, right?

Perhaps Valentine's Day? Why is that? Well, so you can create the right mood for a special night with your lover and have the power to make love successfully, right? That food combination is just for that. Ah, yes, with garlic sauce, too.

However, once we consume it, we will be forced to deal with that energy. Unless we are at the level where we can transform its energy into nothingness, it is wise to restrain from eating it.

If we intend to continue eating this kind of food, it will set back our journey big time. Empty of energy, unfocused, blurry vision, unstable body system—how are we to go straight on? Until these negative food energies are released from our system, we will not be able to continue.

This is not about right or wrong. It is merely to point out the importance of cause and effect that occurs in our life's journey—the way we can follow certain habits without even realizing it.

As we are on a practice journey, how will what we eat affect our practice? We will be filled with that energy. Our focus is no longer sharp, like it was before we consumed the food.

Some false owners would claim that they can eat whatever they want, and it won't affect their practice at all. They say it because they don't care, or they don't know.

Why should they? Since they are not true owners, they have no responsibility for what wrong or damage they create. They think they can enjoy whatever they want without consequences. As far as they're concerned, it's not their problem. As owners, it's up to us to safeguard the energy that we need to reach our destination.

Making poor choices about what we eat causes so much unnecessary suffering on our journey. Once we consume these things, it's a very difficult time to endure for most practitioners. If we are aware, we know never to eat this kind of food, especially at such a crucial time. But habits and karma want to repeat over and over. Who's going to put a stop to these patterns? We can—and we will.

If some of us can erase or transform certain food energy to nothingness, we should still avoid consuming them during practice times, as we will waste a lot of time and effort dealing with it day and night.

If we eat certain foods, those food energies become strong in us—they can even become our second nature.

What's Beef Effect?

If we consume too much beef regularly, we gain the cow's energy and traits. Its energy pervades our system—its thinking and its habits become our second nature. Then who is driving the body?

A beef meal will stay within our system for a long time— days, weeks, even a month, depending on how the body system is. That's how long it stays.

If we consume one beef meal after another, we get heavier and heavier, filled with its toxicity.

It seems that a cow's tendency is to chew and chew, never stop chewing. If we have too much of its toxicity in our system, soon we, too, begin to chew people and things around us, becoming more judgmental and negative. What we eat is what we become.

Cows remember how they died. They were aware of the event. Nobody wants to die on someone's else's terms, including cows. The cows are aware they're going to a slaughterhouse. Cows have their feelings, but nobody cares to listen. They feel anger, injustice, disappointment, and a want for revenge, and these feelings create poison in them when they are killed. That poison is left in the meat and is transferred to us. Before we realize it, we play out a cow's traits and become one with their energy.

So, on our journey, this energy will play out in many ways, becoming anger, negativity, and discontent. Sometimes we may feel pulled in opposite directions; sometimes we might unnecessarily feel like we must fight, even in a casual situation that doesn't call for it. Cows are not happy campers to begin with.

Eating beef affects our journey in every sense, and before meaningful progress can take place, the karma of this consumption must melt away.

If you have consumed beef and are being negatively affected with a cow's traits, try praying for the cow's soul daily.

Cows are living beings. They are very close to humans and easily convert to a human body if they choose in the next life.

That's one of the reasons why certain religions recommend against eating animal meats and fish.

Also, certain ingredients might trigger alterations in our mind and unwanted excitement in our physical body, resulting in an inability to stay calm and in a peaceful state. To be free of these adverse energies, stay free of eating the meats that cause them.

Eating clean food, we can stay in clarity as we continue our journeys.

If someone is taking beef for medicinal purposes, Gingko will help balance this out by providing the lung energy. Take 1-3 tablespoons of Ginkgo a day and mix with juice or water. The taste is not pleasant.

If someone is taking some hormone triggering food, have strong mint tea with roast corn. It will help reduce your agony.

Some people are afraid of the truth. It takes great courage to know ourselves and our body systems.

Four Noble Practices

Suffering Injustice
Adapting to Conditions
Seeking Nothing
Practicing the Dharma

Suffering Injustice: The way we can be distracted by unimportant thoughts is similar to how we can be distracted by pop-ups on the computer—we click on them even though they have no substance. And when we click on them, we can be easily trapped by them, and our suffering begins. These pop-ups can arise from our internal system as thoughts, or they can show up in the external world as enticing desires and promises. Either way, as owner, the power is yours: Simply do not click on them.

Adapting to Conditions: Our curiosity and greed want these external temptations even if they are too good to be true. We want to believe it; we want to taste it. When we are caught in this net of temptations, our suffering will continue.

Seeking Nothing: We already have everything we need within us. There is no reason to seek externally. But because we are not connected to our True Self, we reach, and we click. Once we click, we are in the pop-up's territory. We may realize the mistake and get out quickly, but if we don't, we will be stuck there for a long time, living in that world. We are living but we are no longer living life for ourselves. We are in a pop-up world, bound by its terms and conditions.

Get out of there. We put ourselves into the pop-up world, so we can remove ourselves just the same. Turn within.

<u>Practicing the Dharma:</u> Come back to the essence.

If we remain grounded in our essence, and do not follow our pop-up thoughts, the suffering will no longer be there.

Internal and external distractions can lead us to a world of continuous suffering. Acknowledge and let go.

We must investigate and reflect on ourselves, and on how most of our suffering is created by following pop-ups away from our true essence.

Focusing on the Koan, "What is this?" will cut away all this internal and external clutter and allow us to return to the present moment.

Another helpful practice is to follow the Noble Eightfold Path to freedom.

The Noble Eightfold Path

Right Understanding

Right Thought

Right Speech

Right Action

Right Livelihood

Right Effort

Right Mindfulness

Right Concentration

Thankful Prayers

Pray to be thankful for everything we have and everything we don't have. There's so much we can be thankful for. No begging!

Be thankful for others. Be thankful for their good, bad, and terrible existences. They provide us with learning tools so we can steer ourselves towards the good and away from the terrible. We can learn and upgrade ourselves. No negotiation!

Pray for anyone who we might have inadvertently caused harm in this life or an unknown life. Wish them good health and happiness.
Ask them for forgiveness sincerely, but without begging or negotiating. Be empty-minded about it. Then let the whole thing go. Release it from our system. Let it go and live in freedom from it.

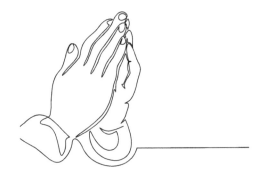

Something's Holding Up Our Progress

We're almost about to reach our destination—we can just see the top—when something happens to halt our journey, or, worse, bring us back down.

As far as we can tell, we've done everything right so far. Yet, something has caused our progress to halt.

This can be any number of things:

a) <u>Lost Awareness:</u> One of the possibilities is that we lost awareness along the way. Following just one pop-up can be enough to get us off-course, lost, and uncertain how to proceed. Once we joined in with a pop up, we lost our awareness.

b) <u>Wrong Food Intake or Eating at the Wrong Time:</u> This can cause imbalance in our body system. Certain foods contain many hormones or can trigger hormonal responses in our body system. During this period, avoid foods that contain many hormones. Also, avoid eating heavy food and eating after 5 pm.

Practice endurance and temperance.

It helps to drink lots of strong mint tea.

c) <u>Guard Your Energy</u>: With practice, a lot of energy may have accumulated in the system—we must beware not to waste this energy through anger and sexual activity. With so much purified energy, it's hard to control it and not be overcome by sexual desire, but we must practice temperance. Remember, we need that energy to carry us to the top and open the door that reveals who we truly are.

It helps to drink lots of strong mint tea.

d) <u>Tasks Are Incomplete, or Debts Are Due:</u> Something on your to-do list remains to be done.

If we realize something needs to be taken care, then we must get it done before we can continue. It's as simple as that. There are no other alternatives.

If the job is not completed, then our journey is on halt no matter how much we want to reach the top.

e) <u>Sexual Activity</u>: Sexual activity during this period will bring us down big time—way down. With sexual activity, we have wasted extremely valuable energy we need to reach the top. Since we used up the energy and are now hollow in the energy tank, we need to wait for enough energy to be re-accumulated to continue our journey.

If our body system is not stable and does not have a strong foundation, refraining from sexual activity can be extremely difficult. Build a stronger foundation and practice endurance and temperance.

How the Universe Helps Us

When the universe changes its energy pattern and fills what we lack in energy, suddenly, with clarity, we will get the deeper meaning and broad spectrum of things that we didn't experience before. This experience is refreshing and uplifting.

For practitioners, when the cycle is favorable, it's a harvest time for spiritual upgrades.

Don't wait for it, though. When we do, it will hinder the outcome. Practice as usual. We will know what to do when the time comes. Entrust everything to the True Self /True Essence/God Sense/ Buddha Nature—there are so many names for it. Be awake. Allow it to reveal itself to us.

It may take one day, many weeks, many months, many years, many lifetimes later—something clicks, and everything seems to fit in place. Finally, we will get it.

Be humble.

Excess Energy for Some

However, some practitioners may not be able to handle all of the favorable energy that the universe is pouring into them at this time, and so they are no longer in the spotlight as before. The spotlight moved in a different direction and waited for another turn.

If we are not Zen practitioners and are living an ordinary life, when a favorable universal cycle shines on us, we may experience many different positive outcomes. We may get promoted, get married, become rich or famous, prosper, be well-treated by others. Things are going very well—so well that we can sometimes forget that other people might not be doing as well. Make sure we are kind to others when we are in this cycle. It will end before we know it. When the cycle ends, it may be us who will need kindness from others.

What is a favorable cycle to some people might affect other people negatively. These people may suddenly find things going downhill, they may become poor, bankrupt, have legal issues, health problems—even death.

Following the body system diet keeps you grounded and stable. How strictly we follow the diet will minimize the size of the ups and downs.

If a person lives modestly, practices charity, and is good to others, they will be less damaged when the cycle is no longer favorable.

Because we don't understand these cycles, it seems like it happens all of a sudden. We look for someone to blame. But there's no one to blame. If anyone, we should blame ourselves for our ignorance. It's crucial to understand these basic cycles so we can have a smoother journey—especially those who do not turn within to access their wisdom.

The universe runs on cycles like clockwork. It's a very precise system. So is our body system—it runs with precision as well. Our mind has a problem of holding on and getting stuck. We need to be better informed and get up-to-date information from the cycle.

The universal system has no discrimination. Everyone can benefit when it comes to their cycle. Be humble so you can receive and seize the moment!

With heavy karma in place, there's no room in your body system for positive universal energy to enter. When that happens, ignorant people try to change this fact, but they can't. First, we must shed our heavy karma to make space for it.

If we can turn our focus within, all wisdom is readily available. But we are used to relying on external information, which is outdated by the time we want to use it.

For the best, most current information, we must do some form of meditation or chanting to clear away the mumbo jumbo and access this inner truth.

Zen is the most direct and quick way to reach this inner well of wisdom. However, when our body is out of balance, we may not get the access to the wisdom we need. Take action to restore your body's balance right now.

The Favorable Cycle

When we are prepared for the cycle, the spotlight is on us. We practice as usual, but when the cycle turns in our favor, our practice starts to pick up without apparent reason.

Our body system becomes fully charged; all the mumbo jumbo and mental chatter is no longer there. We feel no more deficiency.

We will be able decode and understand beyond anything we experienced in the past. We will be able to comprehend what's unfolding before our eyes.

Experience it and acknowledge it. Do not shift back to the old ego system. The ego system might try to come and take over the experience. Don't let it.

The owner should oversee the experience, maintaining a gentle yet attentive awareness.

If we had misunderstandings in the past with associates, friends, or family, suddenly there is room to mend these issues. That is a natural process. Take it humbly, though.

The process may take one day, many weeks, many months, many years, or many lifetimes—something clicks, and everything seems to fit in place. Finally, we get it.

When the cycle is favorable to us, know that it will only last a certain period, not forever—even though it feels like it can go on forever.

Use it as wisely as we can. Once the cycle moves on, the spotlight is no longer on us. But when we live humbly and kindly and help others in need during this period, the effect will carry us a long time. The spotlight will turn to others whom we might have provided help, and they will remember and act kindly toward us.

That's a wise and good investment—especially when we don't have harmonized body structures to harness and keep it all.

Timing

The universe runs in cycles, providing for everyone without discrimination.

Do we know when it will happen?

The timing may vary depending on a person's purpose in their life and their body structures.

Check to be sure that all the missing links in our body system are connected and fastened properly for the special event.

When we are ready with a sincerity that the Universe can recognize as genuine, the door will be opened.

Stay awake and keep your eyes open!

Be humble!!!

How Long Will Enlightenment Take?

It all depends on our readiness. Enlightenment might take a split second, one day, three days, five days, seven days, six months, two years, twenty years, or twenty lifetimes. We will get it when we get it.

We must be 100% present and face ourselves with brutal honesty. No compromise, no hiding, no cheating, no lying, no playing, no delaying, no fearing, no dreaming away. We must face who we are.

After we have faced up to these faulty parts of ourselves, they no longer have any power over us. Now, only the owner remains, standing in front of the special portal. Only the owner can enter and have this experience.

No one can give us that experience. We alone must walk through the gate.

The Special Invitation

Entrance Only Permitted to True Owners

With sincere practice, one can get the ultimate reward.

There are many ways to reach the destination, but the fastest is through Zen practice.

Why is that? It's as straightforward as it gets.

When our practice is devoted and sincere and we reach our destination, we may receive a Special Invitation to reside in a special heavenly place. But this will only happen if you are truly in accord with the following guidelines:

- Practice turning inward sincerely.
- Practice diligently daily.
- Practice deep dedication.
- Practice the four noble truths.
- Practice the eight noble practices.
- Practice connecting to your inner self day and night.
- Be prepared to shed all false "I" if you haven't already, and stay one with your True Essence.
- Be aware and be humble.

Entrance is only permitted to True Owners. This can't be expressed enough.

So many smart people with so much knowledge and trickery and many other qualifications tried and were hoping to enter. They failed.

Our ego, knowledge, and animal instinct can't enter. We cannot enter with an "I."

Many teachers from past to present reiterate that when given a chance with a special invitation, be selfless.

The invitation comes to those who are prepared for it. And the heavens can recognize our sincerity and readiness and open the door for us. But without completing our required practice, the door will not open.

When we stay awake, we will know the door is open, and we will know what to do.

When we reach the gate, our journey is not quite over. We still have a choice to make: To be a sentient being, with a life of suffering, or to enter Buddhahood/God's land.

Don't look back. We have already lived a sentient being's life so many times with so much confusion and suffering.

Instead, go straight ahead to Buddha's Land. Enter Heaven's Gates.

We can't fathom the experience until we reach it and experience it for ourselves. Once we've experienced it, we can't tell others what we experienced for our own protection. It's imperative we stay silent of the experience and continue the journey with deeper meditation.

However, if we need Confirmation, consult with awakened ones or Zen masters to know for sure if the experience is genuine.

What's Comes After the Enlightenment Experience?

Original and spontaneous wisdom.

安 The End

Printed in the USA
CPSIA information can be obtained
at www.ICGtesting.com
LVHW050721091223
765933LV00075B/1694

9 798988 392187